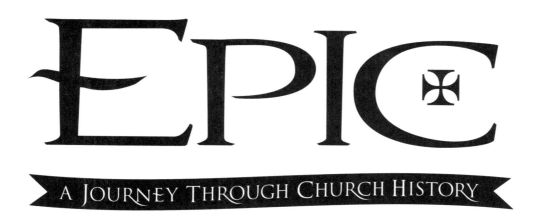

EPIC

A Journey Through Church History

STUDY SET

QUESTIONS & RESPONSES

Steve Weidenkopf & Dr. Alan Schreck

Ascension Press

West Chester, Pennsylvania

Nihil obstat: Rev. Joseph T. Shenosky, S.T.D.
           Censor Librorum
           May 21, 2009

Imprimatur: +Justin Cardinal Rigali
           Archbishop of Philadelphia
           May 22, 2009

Epic: A Journey Thorough Church History is an adult faith formation resource of Ascension Press.

Published by Ascension Press
Post Office Box 1990
West Chester, PA 19380
Orders: 1-800-376-0520
www.AscensionPress.com
www.CatholicTimeline.com

Cover design: Devin Schadt

Printed in the United States of America

ISBN 978-1-934217-50-4

CONTENTS

Please read the instructions in this overview before you continue to the first lesson, which is found in Session 1 Questions, *Introduction & Mustard Seed*.

Course Overview

This workbook augments the *Epic: A Journey through Church History* study by guiding you through your twenty-week adventure learning the story of the Catholic Church. Over the next several weeks, you will:

- Learn about the major people, places, and events of the past two-thousand years in Church history

- Know the twelve time periods of Church history with the unique color-coded system

- Learn the true story of the Crusades

- Understand the rationale for the medieval inquisitors and the Spanish Inquisition

- Discover the revolutionary character of the Protestant Reformation

- Know the real story of the confrontation between Galileo and the Church

- Discover the massive persecution of Christians in the twentieth century

- Learn about the workings of the Holy Spirit throughout Church history

In this study, you will learn the story of the Church through a video or audio presentation by Church history professor Steve Weidenkopf, followed by group discussion. Supplementary materials (including responses to the questions, a full-color chart, and a bookmark) are used to reinforce the lesson and will help you remember the Church's story for years to come.

Materials

Before you begin, make sure you have the following materials for each participant:

- Copies of the *Epic* Church History Timeline Chart and Bookmark

- A copy of the *Epic* 20-Week Seminar Workbook/Study Set

Course Outline

Session	Title
1.	Introduction & Mustard Seed
2.	Persecution – Part I
3.	Persecution – Part II
4.	Conversion & Councils – Part I
5.	Conversion & Councils – Part II
6.	Missionaries & the Emperor – Part I
7.	Missionaries & the Emperor – Part II
8.	Crusaders & Scholars – Part I
9.	Crusaders & Scholars – Part II
10.	Crusaders & Scholars – Part III
11.	Weak Leaders & Schism – Part I
12.	Weak Leaders & Schism – Part II
13.	Protestors & Defenders – Part I
14.	Protestors & Defenders – Part II
15.	Catholic Reformation – Part I
16.	Catholic Reformation – Part II
17.	Revolutions and Modernism
18.	A World at War
19.	The New Springtime
20.	The Threshold of Hope & Conclusion

Order of Study

Participants should prepare for each session by first reading Section A ("Establish the Context") in their Student Workbooks. For each session, watch the appropriate DVD presentation (or listen to the audio CD) and then use the Study Workbook to discuss the questions. Use the blank space under the Learn the Story section for each session to record key events and your thoughts while watching the DVD (or listening to the audio CD).

Answering the Questions

Each session is divided into the following parts:

A. Establish the Context

This section prepares you to learn Church history by providing background information on the specific time period.

B. Learn the Story

The next step is to watch the DVD (or listen to the audio CD) presentation and learn the story of the Church by time period.

Your focus should be to remember the main events of each time period; by doing so, you will come to know the story of the Church. Church history is full of many personalities and events. It can be very difficult to remember every little detail, so don't fret if you can't remember whether it was Henry II or Henry III. Instead, focus on learning the "big picture" of what is happening. *Epic* presents Church history in a narrative way so that you can learn, remember, and identify with the story of the Church. As a result, *Epic* does not give every historical detail or discuss every event; only the major events that tell the story of the Church are covered. Additional studies that will delve deeper into each time period are forthcoming.

C. Take a Deeper Look

Catholic historian and writer Hilaire Belloc wrote of a "Catholic conscience of history," which is "an intimate knowledge through identity." What he meant by this was that every Catholic, because his or her "identity" is one with the Church, should have knowledge of Church history. Of course, Belloc knew that not every Catholic intimately knows the story of the Church. He knew well that the story of the Church is not taught by the culture she shaped. In many ways, our culture has lost the story and is weakened as a result. We must learn the story.

The discussion questions in this section are designed to help you learn and remember the two-thousand-year story of the Church. If, in the course of your discussion, other questions come up, write them down and have someone in the group research them and discuss them next time. (For help in answering questions, you can contact us at www.catholictimeline.com.)

Important Note: Do not look at the recommended answers contained in the back of this workbook before answering them on your own, and if possible, wait until after you have discussed them in a group. (You can read them as a review the next week before the next lesson.)

D. Application

Church history is important because "the past gives meaning to the present and the present determines the future."[1] By studying Church history, we learn the story of our Catholic forebears, those brave men and women who answered God's call to spread the Gospel. In so doing they not only brought the saving mission of Jesus to the far corners of the world, they also built the greatest civilization in world history. We are the beneficiaries of their activity, spiritually and temporally.

---

1   Archbishop Charles J. Chaput, O.F.M. Cap., *Living the Catholic Faith*.

We, too, have a part to play in the story of the Church. Each lesson contains one question at the end that asks you to think about how the lessons of history apply to today – either to the Church, to society, or to you. After answering that question, spend time with God in prayer.

E. Wrap-up

Each lesson concludes with a wrap-up section to help you remember the main theme of the time period. This is a brief yet very important step in learning the story!

F. Further Reading (optional)

There is much to learn about Church history. For those who want to pursue outside readings, this section provides a list of good books whose authors approach the subject of Church history and Western civilization from a Catholic worldview.

May God be with you on this journey, and may you grow closer to His Church as a result of your study.

Introduction & Mustard Seed

A. Establish the Context

"The Church ... believes that the key, the center, and the purpose of the whole of man's history is to be found in its Lord and Master."

– *Catechism of the Catholic Church*, 450

Introduction – What is history?

When you hear the word "history," what comes to mind: the recitation of past events, the memorization of dates, a boring subject from high school or college, or a rousing story that helps explain the world we live in? Unfortunately, for many, the latter is not often the image that springs to mind. History is much more than the memorization of dates; it is God's theater, the place where He makes known His-story. History is the story of God at work in the world and of the men and women He has called to play leading roles in the divine drama. More specifically, Church history is the story of that great organization, founded by Christ, to spread His Gospel throughout the world. Knowing our history, especially the history of the Church, is crucial to our future, since we cannot shape it without an adequate understanding of the past. As Catholics, Church history offers us insight into who we are, where we have come from, and where we are going.

The story of the Church shapes our identity as Catholics. We are the inheritors of the deeds of great men and women who for two-thousand years have built a great civilization and spread the Gospel throughout the world. Today, unfortunately, one sees an "identity crisis" among many Catholics who do not know the story of the Church nor the role she has played in building Western civilization. In order to know ourselves as Catholics, we need to know the epic story of the Church and the civilization she built.

The authentic story of the Church has rarely been told over recent years. Many of us are at a loss to tell the story of the Church when confronted by misinformation and prejudice. In order to combat the counter-story, we must be armed with the truth of Church history and given the tools to remember that story.

Before you embark on the epic journey of learning the history of the Church, here are some things that you should keep in mind:

1. The Central Event of Human History

Catholics believe that history is not a random series of events; rather, it is the story of God working in the world through His Church and His people. There is a beginning (creation) and an end (the Second Coming)

> There are two ways, one of life and one of death: and great is the difference between the two ways.
>
> – The *Didache*

to history. Moreover, there is one central event upon which the whole of human history hinges, the Incarnation. The coming of the God-man and its saving implications is an event that radiates backward and forward in human history.

2.   *The Mystery of the Church*

The Church is a mystery that is visible and invisible. "The Church is in history, but at the same time she transcends it. It is only 'with the eyes of faith' that one can see her in her visible reality and at the same time in her spiritual reality as bearer of divine life" (*Catechism of the Catholic Church*, 770). Although, in the study of Church history, we gaze predominantly on the visible element, we must also ponder that which we see "with the eyes of faith."

3.   *The Purpose of the Church*

Christ founded the Church for one purpose: to continue His saving work. The Church has no mission outside of Christ—it is not her mission, but His. As Jesus ascended into Heaven, He commanded His apostles to preach and teach the Good News (cf. Mt 28: 19). Evangelization and catechesis are the primary actions of the Church, and throughout history she has expended great energy in fulfilling that divine commission.

4.   *The Church Is Holy yet Contains Sinners*

History involves the actions of persons endowed with the gift of free will. Sometimes those actions are in accord with God's law, and sometimes they are not. The Church—established by God, imbued with the Holy Spirit, and comprised of the triumphant saints in heaven—is holy, yet she also contains sinners. Throughout history there have been those, even among the holders of the highest office, who have not acted in a holy manner. This should not be a reason to turn from the Church; rather, it should be a reason to rejoice in the fact that the Holy Spirit is truly present in the Church and has guided her in good times and bad.

5.   *What's in a Name?*

The names of things are very important, and the language we use bespeaks our perspective. For example, saying someone is "anti-abortion" as opposed to "pro-life" says something about the person using the term. In history, this is also true. History in the United States has been traditionally presented through the lens of English Protestantism, and for many of us, this perspective has shaped our understanding of historical persons and events. For example, most history books treat Elizabeth I as the good "Virgin Queen" of England—never mentioning the hundreds of Catholic priests and lay men and women she killed. Additionally, her half-sister Mary is known as "Bloody Mary" for her persecution of Protestants— however, her desire and actions to restore England to the Faith is never mentioned. It is important to know our history and to use the terms that accurately describe it.

6.   *History Doesn't Repeat Itself, It Rhymes*

Catholics don't believe that history is one endless cycle of repeating events or even that we are "doomed" to repeat past mistakes. Rather, human history is living and dynamic and is moving toward the final fulfillment. However, the careful student of Church history will find events that rhyme, where the action of God is very discernible and things happen in the past that set the stage for future events.

The Mustard Seed

It is ten days since they saw Jesus ascend into glory and fifty days since His Resurrection from the dead. The apostles gather together in the Upper Room, and they suddenly hear and feel a mighty wind and see tongues of fire. The Holy Spirit filled that little "band of brothers" on the day of Pentecost two thousand years ago. This event marks the beginning of the Catholic Church, God's chosen instrument of salvation. It is in a room in Jerusalem that the organization that would build a civilization and nurture billions of people is born.

The Twelve are commissioned by Christ and emboldened by the Holy Spirit to go into the world spreading the Gospel. Most go beyond the confines of the Roman Empire; some stay within it and bring the Gentiles into the fold. The Church soon suffers persecution and the first martyr, St. Stephen, is called to give his life for Christ. A man who originally persecutes the Church is miraculously converted and becomes a tireless preacher of the Faith, traveling extensively to bring the Good News to the Gentiles. His missionary efforts produce much fruit and lead to the first discussion of Church discipline. The apostles gather in Jerusalem to discuss how to handle the infusion of non-Jewish converts: Are they subject to the Law of Moses or not? After listening to both arguments, St. Peter provides the answer and the first definitive statement of Church discipline. The development of doctrine and liturgy is also noticeable during this time period and recorded in the *Didache* (or *The Teaching of the Twelve Apostles*).

The Emperor Nero uses Christians in Rome as human torches after the burning of the city in A.D. 64. The apostles Peter and Paul meet their martyrdom during this persecution. This is the first of many government-sanctioned persecutions that will span the next three centuries. Following the persecution of the Emperor Domitian, the pope intervenes in a dispute in the Church of Corinth. Pope St. Clement's letter to the Corinthians in A.D. 96 illustrates the primacy of the Roman pontiff during the earliest days of the Church. The Mustard Seed period ends with the death of the last and most beloved apostle, St. John; the Church is still a small, but growing, organization. In the next period, the Church will continue to grow even in the face of severe and cruel persecution.

B. Learn the Story

View Track 1, *Introduction* & *Mustard Seed,* of the *Epic: A Journey through Church History* 20-Week Study DVD (or listen to the audio CD). Follow the presentation by referring to your *Epic* Church History Timeline Chart.

N O T E S

NOTES

C. Take a Deeper Look

Answering these questions will help you learn the story of the Church. If other questions come to mind write them down to discuss in the group.

Introduction: What is history?

1.   Why do we like stories? Why are they important to us?

2.   Jesus spoke to His disciples in parables. List some of these parables. Which is your favorite? Why?

3.   Is history important? Why should we study it?

4.   Hilaire Belloc spoke of a "Catholic conscience of history." What is this? Do you have it? If so, how did you acquire it? If not, why not?

5.   As Catholics, how do we understand history?

Mustard Seed

1.   What event marks the beginning of the Church? What happened?

2.   What was the major topic of discussion at the Council of Jerusalem? How was the issue resolved?

3.   Why did the persecution of Christians erupt in A.D. 64? Was the persecution widespread? What was its effect?

4.   What are the key points raised in Pope St. Clement's letter to the Corinthians?

Nero's Persecution as Told by Tacitus

But neither human help, nor imperial munificence … could stifle scandal or dispel the belief that the fire had taken place by order. Therefore, to scotch the rumor, Nero substituted as culprits, and punished with the utmost refinements of cruelty, a class of men, loathed for their vices, whom the crowd styled Christians. Christus, the founder of the name, had undergone the death penalty in the reign of Tiberius, by sentence of the procurator Pontius Pilate, and the pernicious superstition was checked for a moment, only to break out once more, not merely in Judea, the home of the disease, but in the capital itself, where all things horrible or shameful in the world collect and find a vogue. First, then, the confessed members of the sect were arrested; next, on their disclosures, vast numbers were convicted … They were covered with wild beasts' skins and torn to death by dogs; or they were fastened on crosses, and, when daylight failed, were burned to serve as lamps by night. Nero had offered his gardens for the spectacle, and gave an exhibition in his circus mixing with the crowd in the habit of a charioteer or mounted on his car. Hence, in spite of the guilt which had earned the most exemplary punishment, there arose a sentiment of pity, due to the impression that they were being sacrificed not for the welfare of the state but to the ferocity of a single man.

– *Annals* XV, 44

D. Application

This question asks you to think about how the lessons of history apply to today – either to the Church, to society, or to you. After meditating on this question, spend time with God in prayer.

The apostles went beyond the known world to begin the spread of the Gospel. How were they able to accomplish such a feat? What was your journey of faith? Who first brought the Gospel to your attention? How have you helped spread the Gospel?

Dear Lord …

E. Wrap-up

Conclude your study of the Mustard Seed period and remember the main events by doing the following:

1. What is the color of this time period? How can you remember it?

2. What is the main theme of this period?

3. Write a one- or two-sentence summary of the Mustard Seed period in order to recall the main events of Church history during this time.

F. Further Reading

For those who want to pursue outside readings, here is a list of good books that cover this time period, whose authors approach the subject of Church history and Western civilization from a Catholic worldview. This list is not exhaustive but is provided as a starting point. Happy reading!

Acts of the Apostles. *Scripture gives us the story of the early Church, highlighting the activities of Saints Peter and Paul.*

Belloc, Hilaire. *Europe and the Faith.* Rockford, IL: TAN Books and Publishers, Inc., 1992. *An excellent essay of how the Church saved and built Western civilization and the importance of the Church to Europe.*

Cavins, Jeff. *Acts: The Spread of the Kingdom.* West Chester, PA: Ascension Press, 2006. *Scripture teacher Cavins provides a foundational study on the Acts of the Apostles, exploring how the Church continues Christ's mission.*

Clark, Kenneth. *Civilisation.* New York: Harper & Row, 1969. *A history of Western civilization utilizing art. Very perceptive review of historical events and the shaping of culture. This book is a companion to the BBC television series, which is available on DVD.*

Sienkiewicz, Henryk. *Quo Vadis.* Translated by W. S. Kuniczak. New York: Hippocrene Books, 1993. *A work of fiction that provides a vivid description of early Christians in the Roman Empire through a compelling and riveting narrative.*

Whitehead, Kenneth D. *One, Holy Catholic, and Apostolic: The Early Church was the Catholic Church.* San Francisco: Ignatius Press, 2000. *An excellent apologetic work on proving that the early Christian Church was one, holy, catholic, and apostolic—which are the marks of the Catholic Church.*

Persecution – Part I

A. Establish the Context

"Remember the word that I said to you, 'A servant is not greater than his master.' If they persecuted me, they will persecute you."

– John 15:20

The Roman Empire was in chaos. Endless struggles over the imperial throne had created lasting instability within the government. From A.D. 192 to 284, a period of only ninety-two years, twenty-eight different emperors reigned, and of them, twenty-two were murdered. Conflict with the Persians in the East, as well as squabbles with barbarians and pirates on the fringes of the Empire, created an atmosphere of constant turbulence. Within this disorder, the Church was surviving.

The Church was a unique organization within the Roman Empire. As the letters of St. Ignatius of Antioch (martyred in A.D. 115) testify, she was not some loose association of "all believers" who vaguely shared a few principles of faith but a highly organized and disciplined body with her own officers and doctrine.

During this time, the persecutions begun by Nero and Domitian continued but were interspersed with periods of indifference or tolerance, and during these lulls the Church grows. Pagans launch a propaganda campaign of lies and myths to slander Christians. Often calamities throughout the empire, like barbarian invasions or earthquakes, are blamed on Christians, who are consequently sent to their death in the savage public games. Brilliant minds, such as St. Justin Martyr and Tertullian, rise to the challenge, writing skillful defenses of the Faith, and thus the first Christian apologists are born. During this time, the Church also encounters enemies "within the gates," as heretics arise to mislead the faithful and corrupt the apostolic teaching. Champions such as St. Irenaeus rally to preserve the true Faith from any distortions.

The wisdom of
St. Ignatius of Antioch:

"God's wheat I am, and by the teeth of wild beasts I am to be ground that I may prove Christ's pure bread."

"Where the bishop appears, there let the people be, just as where Jesus Christ is, there is the Catholic Church."

NOTES

B. Learn the Story

View Track 2, *Persecution*, of the *Epic: A Journey through Church History* 20-Week Study DVD (or listen to the audio CD). Follow the presentation by referring to your *Epic* Church History Timeline Chart.

NOTES

C. Take a Deeper Look

Answering these questions will help you learn the story of the Church. If other questions come to mind, write them down to discuss in the group.

1. What was the Church in the Roman Empire? Give some of its characteristics.

2. What were some of the pagan myths used to slander the early Church? Are these myths still used today?

3. Why did the Roman Empire persecute the Church? Do you think such persecution could happen in our modern world?

4. St. Ignatius, Bishop of Antioch, wrote seven letters on his way to be martyred in Rome. What are some of the important points made in these early Christian writings?

5. During this time, heresies arose to attack the Church from within. What were some of the early heresies of the Church, and what were some of their mistaken beliefs?

The Persecution of the Early Christians

There were thousands and thousands of people, men with their wives and children, who despised temporal life according to the teaching of our Savior, suffered all kinds of death. Some after bearing the iron hooks, the racks, the whips and other torments innumerable and terrible to hear were finally consigned to the flames; others were drowned in the sea. Still others bravely offered their heads to the executioner, died under torture, or expired from hunger. Some were crucified in the manner used for criminals, and others even more cruelly were fixed to the cross with their head down and left to die of hunger.

– Eusebius, *Hist. Eccl.* VIII, 8

D. Application

This question asks you to think about how the lessons of history apply to today—either to the Church, to society, or to you. After meditating on this question, spend time with God in prayer.

St. Justin Martyr wrote a defense of the Faith to the Roman Emperor Antoninus Pius. Many others rose up to fight the myths and lies being spread about the Christians by Roman society. What are some of the modern-day myths and lies told about the Church and her teachings? Share an experience in which you defended the Faith. What are some effective ways to counter the misrepresentation and misinformation of the Faith in our modern world?

Dear Lord …

Persecution – Part II

A. Establish the Context

"The blood of the martyrs is the seed of Christians."

– Tertullian

For more than 200 years, the Roman Empire has persecuted the Faith. The Church has not disappeared but rather, emboldened by the witness of the martyrs, has continued to grow. The persecutions continue under the selfish rule of several emperors. In the late third century, Diocletian becomes Emperor of Rome and establishes a new order of government. His Tetrarchy, consisting of two co-emperors (Augustuses) and their associated understudies (Caesars), divides the unwieldy empire into two halves (East and West) with more manageable regional portions.

Diocletian works hard to rebuild the crumbling empire and meets with temporary success. While he has no direct animosity towards Christians, at the behest of Galerius, his understudy, he begins what would become the worst of all Roman persecutions of the Church. An empire-wide campaign to completely eradicate the Church is undertaken. Thousands upon thousands of Christians are tortured and killed or sent to be slaves in the mines, a blood-drenched climax to this period of cruel torment and suffering.

Battered from without and sabotaged from within, the Church is sure to be torn apart and trampled into the dust of history. But Christ does not allow it. The persecutions end, and the Church rises from the ashes only to be faced with a serious question: how will she deal with those who gave in during the persecutions and do not maintain the Faith and are now seeking re-entry into the community? Should a strict policy of no re-admittance or one of mercy reign supreme?

Christian response to the persecution:

Traditores
those who gave in

Confessores
the faithful

Lapsi
those who gave in but repented after persecution ended

NOTES

B. Learn the Story

View Track 3, *Persecution – Part II*, of the *Epic: A Journey through Church History* 20-Week Study DVD (or listen to the audio CD). Follow the presentation by referring to your *Epic* Church History Timeline Chart.

NOTES

C. Take a Deeper Look

Answering these questions will help you learn the story of the Church. If other questions come to mind, write them down to discuss in the group.

1. The early Church Fathers defended the Faith by explaining it to the Romans and fighting the errors of heretics. Who were some of these first apologists? Why are they important?

2. Tertullian was one of the great early Church Fathers who defended the Faith from pagan critics. His early work is even quoted in the *Catechism of the Catholic Church*. Yet, despite his brilliance and devotion, he died a heretic. What lessons can we learn from Tertullian's tragic fall?

3.   Overall, there were twelve major persecutions under the Roman Empire. What were the names of some of the emperors who persecuted Christians during this time period? What were the dates and circumstances of these persecutions?

4.   The story of the early Church is filled with the sacrifices of great martyrs. Is there a particular martyr of the early Church whom you admire or relate to? What is his or her story, and how did you first learn about this saint?

5.   Christians presented no real threat to the Roman Empire, since they were, for the most part, tax-paying, law-abiding citizens, yet they were consistently persecuted. St. Justin Martyr explained why by saying, "The world suffers nothing from Christians but hates them because they reject its pleasures." What do you think he meant?

6.   One of the great difficulties the early Church faced was how to deal with *lapsi*, or lapsed Catholics who fell away from the Faith during persecution. Why do you think this was such a difficult problem? Is this a problem in the Church today?

> ### *St. Justin Martyr's Teaching on the Eucharist (A.D. 155)*
>
> We call this food Eucharist; and no one else is permitted to partake of it, except one who believes our teaching to be true and who has been washed in the washing which is for the remission of sins and for regeneration, and is thereby living as Christ has enjoined. For not as common bread nor common drink do we receive these; but since Jesus Christ our Savior was made incarnate by the word of God and had both flesh and blood for our salvation, so too, as we have been taught, the food which has been made into the Eucharist by the Eucharistic prayer set down by Him, and by the change of which our blood and flesh is nourished, is both the flesh and blood of that incarnated Jesus.
>
> – *First Apology*, 65

D. Application

This question asks you to think about how the lessons of history apply to today – either to the Church, society or to you. After meditating on this question, spend time with God in prayer.

"The blood of martyrs is the seed of Christians," said Tertullian. Persecution was the ultimate test for the early Christians. Many martyrs, like St. Perpetua, went to their death while their close friends and families pleaded with them to turn away from their faith and save their lives. Often, the only thing asked of them was to offer one tiny pinch of incense to an idol, but they refused to compromise their faith. While the modern world, in most cases, does not openly persecute Christians, it does encourage us to make small compromises with our faith so as not to offend others. How are you called to suffer for the Faith in today's world? What can you do to foster a faith that will never compromise?

Dear Lord …

E. Wrap-up

Conclude your study of the Persecution period and remember the main events by doing the following:

1. What is the color of this time period? How can you remember it?

2. What is the main theme of this period?

3. Write a one- or two-sentence summary of the Persecution period in order to recall the main events of Church history during this time.

F. Further Reading

For those who want to pursue outside readings, here is a list of good books that cover this time period whose authors approach the subject of Church history and Western civilization from a Catholic worldview. This list is not exhaustive but is provided as a starting point. Happy reading!

Carroll, Warren H. *The Founding of Christendom.* Front Royal, VA: Christendom Press, 1985. *Volume 1 of a planned six-volume work. This is a scholarly read with great detail and an excellent and well-documented work.*

Newman, John Cardinal. *Callista.* Cosimo Classics, 2007. *A work of historical fiction that focuses on the Roman persecutions in Northern Africa and seamlessly weaves fictional characters with true historical persons.*

Ricciotti, Giuseppe. *The Age of Martyrs.* Rockford, IL: TAN Books and Publishers, Inc., 1999. *An easy-to-read and well-documented history of the great persecution under Diocletian. It gives a broad historical and political background, as well as specific details on the stories of individual martyrs.*

Conversion & Councils – Part I

A JOURNEY THROUGH CHURCH HISTORY

A. Establish the Context

In hoc signo vinces. ("In this sign, you shall conquer.")

One man fulfilling the destiny ordained for him by God can change history. Never has this been illustrated more clearly than in the life of the Roman Emperor Constantine the Great. Son of the Western Augustus, Constantius, Constantine is declared Emperor by the Western Army upon the death of his father. However, another, more powerful claimant to the throne, Maxientius, holds Rome. Against the advice of his generals, Constantine decides to march on Rome and bring Maxientius' legions to battle. On the march, Constantine's army is stunned by a mysterious vision in the sky, a cross with the words *In hoc signo vinces* ("In this sign, you shall conquer") surrounding it. Believing this to be a sign from the Christian God announcing a great victory, Constantine has his soldiers paint the Greek monogram for Christ, the Chi Rho, on their shields. Never before in history has an army marched to battle with the insignia of Christ. Although vastly outnumbered, Constantine's warriors win a great victory at the Milvian Bridge on October 28, 312. This victory will ultimately bring about the conversion of the Empire, previously the great enemy of the Faith.

A year later, Constantine and the Eastern Augustus, Licinius, bring an end to the Roman persecutions with the Edict of Milan, which legalizes the Faith in the Empire. Constantine takes up the Christian cause with zeal, and new churches and statues spring up across the Empire as wealth, land, and civil rights are returned to the long-suffering Christians. To better rule the vast empire, Constantine moves the capital to a more central city, Byzantium, now renamed Constantinople. Throughout his reign, Constantine will meddle in the affairs of the Church, establishing a dangerous precedent that causes conflict in the Empire and the Church for centuries to come. Overall, Constantine will be a great proponent of the Church and eventually will become a Christian, being baptized on his deathbed in the year 337.

Facts & Stats:
Number of doctors of the Church in this period = 13 or 40 percent of total

Council of Nicaea vote tally:
Jesus is "one-in-being" with the Father.
For = 316
Against = 2

The liberation brings but brief joy to the Church, as a new terror arises so strong that the Catholic Faith, strengthened by years of persecution, is almost entirely undone. A North African priest, Arius, denies the very divinity of Jesus Christ, a central doctrine of faith. This heresy blazes across the empire like brushfire. Turmoil and unrest are the result of this radical teaching. Constantine steps in and calls the Catholic bishops together, the first time in history that all are invited to such a gathering. The first Ecumenical Council of Nicaea (325) solemnly condemns Arianism, but its defeat is not total; it will strike back with a vengeance.

During the persecutions, many are called to shed their blood for Christ. After legalization, the threat of active persecution diminishes; instead, Christians develop the living of a "white" martyrdom—dying to self and the world for love of God. These "white" martyrs, led by St. Anthony the Abbot in Egypt, became known as monks, and they shaped the very history of the Church and Western civilization.

B. Learn the Story

View Track 4, *Conversion & Councils – Part I*, of the *Epic: A Journey through Church History* 20-Week Study DVD (or listen to the audio CD). Follow the presentation by referring to your *Epic* Church History Timeline Chart.

NOTES

C. Take a Deeper Look

Answering these questions will help you learn the story of the Church. If other questions come to mind, write them down to discuss in the group.

1. One historian has remarked that Constantine gave the world the vision of what a Christian emperor could be. What is your assessment of Constantine and his relationship with the Church?

2. The Edict of Milan is one of the most significant events in Church history. When was it issued? What did it accomplish? Why do you think it was important?

3. Arianism plagued the Church for more than 300 years. What were the basic tenets of this heresy? Does it still exist today?

4. Popular books and movies often claim that Constantine completely transformed the Church. In particular, it is said that Constantine imposed the idea that Jesus Christ was God and established the hierarchical order of the Church. Can you refute this error based on what you've learned about Church history?

5. As Emperor, Constantine was very involved in Church affairs. How do you think that precedent influenced Church history? How do political leaders approach the Church in our modern time? What is the proper role of the Church in politics?

6. The Council of Nicaea was the first ecumenical council of the Church. What was the major discussion at the council? The council produced a negative and positive teaching. What were they?

7. A new form of living the Christian Faith emerged during this time period: monasticism. Where did it originate and why there? With whom? How was it lived?

Exhortation of St. Anthony the Abbot against the Arians

Have no fellowship with the most impious Arians. For there is no communion between light and darkness. For you are good Christians, but they, when they say that the Son of the Father, the Word of God, is a created being, differ not from the heathen, since they worship that which is created, rather than God, the creator. But believe that the Creation itself is angry with them because they number the Creator, the Lord of all, by whom all things came into being, with those things which were originated.

– Athanasius, *Vita S. Antoni*, 69

D. Application

This question asks you to think about how the lessons of history apply to today – either to the Church, to society, or to you. After meditating on this question, spend time with God in prayer.

Christians were finally welcomed into Roman society, but a new host of subtle dangers was waiting for them. The constant threat of persecution had made it easy to stay focused on the Faith, but now the temptation to be "of the world" sapped the zeal of many Catholics. Monasticism responded to this problem. Many chose to leave the world in order to grow closer to Christ in solitude or in community. Are you tempted to be of the world and not just in it? What modern-day distractions threaten your relationship with Christ? What can you do to most take advantage of the time God has graciously given you?

Dear Lord …

EPIC

Conversion & Councils – Part II

A. Establish the Context

"But the Counselor, the Holy Spirit, whom the Father will send in my name, He will teach you all things, and bring to your remembrance all that I have said to you."

– John 14:26

Ten years after the Council of Nicaea, the proponents of Arianism continue to wage their war to overturn the Nicene teachings. They have the ear of the Emperor. The inferno of heresy consumes the majority of Catholic bishops in the East. One man stands in the breach. One man maintains the Faith and refuses to succumb to political pressure; he suffers exile from his diocese five times over almost half a century. The bishop of Alexandria, Egypt, St. Athanasius—the Defender of Orthodoxy—is the lone voice crying out in the desert in order to preserve the authentic Faith of the Church.

While withstanding the plague of Arianism, the Church suffers under the brief rule of the only Christian emperor to apostatize, Julian. Julian restores paganism to the Empire and even unleashes active persecution against Christians and the Church. His hatred of Christ is all-consuming and dominates his short reign. Another Roman emperor, Theodosius, finally outlaws the practice of paganism in the Empire. The conversion of the Empire is now complete.

Faced with an influx of converts since legalization, the Church is beset by numerous false teachings that seek to remake the Faith in a different image. The Holy Spirit animates three important ecumenical councils in which the pope and the bishops forge an authentic expression of the core doctrines of the Faith. The divinity of the Third Person of the Trinity is defended at Constantinople (381). The honor of the Mother of God is championed at Ephesus (431). The two Natures of Christ are confirmed at Chalcedon (451). The Holy Spirit also endows the Church with many of the Church Fathers (St. Augustine, St. Ambrose, St. Jerome, St. Basil the Great, St. John Chrysostom, St. Cyril of Alexandria, and St. Gregory Nazienzen), who cast their theological shadows thousands of years into the future.

Number of times St. Athanasius exiled
5

The end of paganism in the Roman Empire
A.D. 380

Shortest council in Church history
Council of Ephesus
(431) - 1 day

The western half of the Roman Empire is undergoing profound change. Central authority has weakened to the point where Pope St. Leo the Great steps in to ensure the safety of Rome by convincing Attila and his savage Huns not to sack the city. But Rome is exhausted. Alaric, ethnically a Germanic barbarian but a Roman citizen by birth, sacks the city of Rome for the first time in 800 years. Only a short while later, the Western Empire collapses into independently ruled provinces. Of the local chiefs rising up to become kings, all but one are Arian heretics, and the Church is again in danger of being ruled by hostile states.

This period begins and ends with the conversion of pagan warriors who solidify the Faith and protect the Church. Almost 200 years after the rise of Constantine, Clovis, King of the Franks, is called to become a champion for the Faith. Baptized with his warriors on Christmas Day, Clovis becomes the first Catholic king. The territory of the Franks becomes the land of France—the "Eldest Daughter of the Church."

B. Learn the Story

View Track 5, *Conversion & Councils – Part II,* of the *Epic: A Journey through Church History* 20-Week Study DVD (or listen to the audio CD). Follow the presentation by referring to your *Epic* Church History Timeline Chart.

NOTES

C. Take a Deeper Look

Answering these questions will help you learn the story of the Church. If other questions come to mind, write them down to discuss in the group.

1.   Who was St. Athanasius? Can you describe the important role he played in the story of the Church? Describe the persecution he underwent for the Faith. What made him persevere?

2.   Julian the Apostate persecuted the Church after its legalization. Have you been persecuted for your faith? If so, share that experience.

3.   After Nicaea, there were three other ecumenical councils during this time period. When and where were they held? What main aspects of the Faith did each council address? Which heresies did each council condemn?

4. The Roman Empire had persecuted the Church for hundreds of years, and a strong anti-Catholic sentiment thrived amongst the still generally pagan populace, who continued to blame warfare on the frontier and natural disasters on Christians. One might guess that Christians would have celebrated the collapse of the Roman Empire, but this was not the case. How can you explain the sadness that many Catholics, like St. Augustine and St. Jerome, expressed when they saw the demise of Rome?

5. Pope St. Leo I is one of the few popes in all of history to be called "Great." What were some of his significant accomplishments? Why do you think he is called "Great"? What makes a pope "great"?

6. The baptism of Clovis in 496 is another monumental event in Church history. Why is it important?

Paganism outlawed by Theodosius the Great (A.D. 378 – 395)

It is Our will that all the peoples who are ruled by the administration of Our Clemency shall practice that religion which Peter the Apostle transmitted to the Romans ... We command that those persons who follow this rule shall embrace the name of Catholic Christians. The rest, however, whom We adjudge demented and insane, shall sustain the infamy of heretical dogmas, their meeting places shall not receive the name of churches, and they shall be smitten first by divine vengeance and secondly by the retribution of Our own initiative.

– *Theodosian Code XVI, 1, 2*

D. Application

This question asks you to think about how the lessons of history apply to today—either to the Church, to society, or to you. After meditating on this question, spend time with God in prayer.

This time period was witness to four important ecumenical councils during which the Holy Spirit guided the pope and bishops to develop the authentic expression of many of our core doctrinal beliefs. These teachings were necessary to settle theological disputes in the Church so that harmony and unity could reign. Over the centuries, many theological works have been written on the teachings first articulated in this time period. Do you make time to study these and other teachings in order to grow closer to Christ and His Church? Are there teachings of the Church you disagree with? Why? Have you read and reflected on why the Church teaches these things?

Dear Lord …

E. Wrap-up

Conclude your study of the Conversion & Councils period and remember the main events by doing the following:

1. What is the color of this time period? How can you remember it?

2. What is the main theme of this period?

3. Write a one- or two-sentence summary of the Conversion & Councils period in order to recall the main events of Church history during this time.

F. Further Reading

For those who want to pursue outside readings, here is a list of good books that cover this time period and whose authors approach the subject of Church history and Western civilization from a Catholic worldview. This list is not exhaustive but is provided as a starting point. Happy reading!

Carroll, Warren H. *The Building of Christendom.* Front Royal, VA: Christendom Press, 1987. *Volume 2 of a planned six-volume work. This is a scholarly read with great detail. It is an excellent and well-documented work.*

Eusebius - The Church History. Translation and commentary by Paul L. Maier. Grand Rapids, MI: Kregel Publications, 2007. *Eusebius of Caesarea is the father of Church history and lived during some of the most interesting times in history. He chronicles the history of the Church from Apostolic times to the reign of Constantine. Unfortunately, he was sympathetic to Arius and his teachings, but he was a top-notch scholar and his* History *is a classic.*

Augustine, St. *The City of God* and *The Confessions. There are many translations of these two books available (some are even online), and they stand as two of the greatest works by one of the Church's most revered theologians.*

Jurgens, William. *The Faith of the Early Fathers*, 3 vols. Collegeville, MN: The Liturgical Press, 1970, 1979. *A three-volume set that is absolutely indispensable for anyone who wants to learn more about the teachings of the Church Fathers, from Pope St. Clement I to St. John Damascene. It includes an invaluable topical index that spans all three volumes.*

Rengers, Rev. Christopher, O.F.M. Cap. *The 33 Doctors of the Church*. Rockford, IL: TAN Books and Publishers, Inc., 2000. *Contains great biographical info on all thirty-three Doctors of the Church, including St. Athanasius, St. Ambrose, St. Augustine, St. John Chyrsostom, St. Jerome, and more.*

Ricciotti, Giuseppe. *Julian the Apostate*. Rockford, IL: TAN Books and Publishers, Inc., 1999 (reprint). *An interesting look at this fascinating character, the only apostate Christian emperor in history.*

Waugh, Evelyn. *Helena*. Chicago: Loyola Press, 2005. *A fictional novel about Helena, mother of Constantine the Great.*

Missionaries & the Emperor – Part I

A. Establish the Context

"The light shines in the darkness, and the darkness has not overcome it."

– John 1:5

Bereft of its beauty, like an autumn tree facing ominous winter storms, the Roman Empire is in ruins. The loss of a strong unified army strains the seams of civilization as barbarian rampages destroy schools, aqueducts, and even whole villages. Amidst this chaos, St. Benedict becomes the father of Western monasticism. He builds his monastery high upon the hill of Monte Cassino, and his Rule goes forth throughout the Western world to govern the strong but unorganized passion of holy men. Behind these thick walls, hunched over scrawled parchments, monks preserve countless ancient treasures, including Holy Scripture itself.

Among these holy monks hides a humble man who cannot escape his destiny. Thrust into the Chair of Peter by popular demand, St. Gregory the Great quickly becomes the pillar against which all the Western world leans. However, he finds himself not only governing the Church, but with the collapse of central government, he finds himself also governing the city of Rome. So with great zeal he disciplines clergy, enforces clerical celibacy, establishes hospitals, organizes armies, fends off barbarians, defends the papacy from Eastern usurpers, feeds the hungry (often at his own table), revitalizes the liturgy, and fights heresies, all while writing over 800 letters and several monumental treatises. A chance encounter in the slave market, where Angle youths are called "Angels," inspires him to send St. Augustine of Canterbury to lead a missionary expedition to convert the British, and between this Apostle of England and the Irish monks taught by St. Patrick, the whole country is brought into the Church. Having been plagued with painful illnesses throughout his entire pontificate, this tireless Servant of the Servants of God finally finds eternal rest in 604.

But from the East looms a threat that blots out the sun like a sandstorm. Rising with the harsh desert winds is a man who inspires millions to wage a never-ending battle against Christ and His Church. Mohammed strips every vestige of divinity from Jesus Christ, and soon his followers strip the ancient Sees away from the Church. Egypt, Antioch, Jerusalem, and even the entire Iberian peninsula fall, and in less than a hundred years half of all Christian land and wealth dwells under the crescent moon. Trudging into France, the Muslim horde hopes to force the whole world to submit to "Allah's will." But the scimitar is finally smashed by the "hammer" of the Franks, Charles Martel. At the Battle of Poitiers (732), he stops the Muslim advance, and soon his son, Pepin, wrests the legacy of Clovis from the limp hands of the "do-nothing" Merovingians. All is now set for the great emperor to take the stage.

The life of a Benedictine monk:
ora et labora
("pray and work")

English baptized on Christmas Day 597 by St. Augustine of Canterbury and companions
10,000

Number of Mohammed's wives
14

St. Gregory I
(590-604)

B.   Learn the Story

View Track 6, *Missionaries & the Emperor – Part I,* of the *Epic: A Journey through Church History* 20-Week Study DVD (or listen to the audio CD). Follow the presentation by referring to your *Epic* Church History Timeline Chart.

NOTES

C. Take a Deeper Look

Answering these questions will help you learn the story of the Church. If other questions come to mind write them down to discuss in the group.

1. Why is St. Benedict known as the father of Western monasticism? Explain, in your own words, his vision of monasticism.

2. Pope St. Gregory I is another of the few popes to be awarded the title of "Great." What were some of his achievements? Does he share anything in common with Pope St. Leo the Great?

3. Despite the many difficulties of this time period, missionary activity thrived. Who were some of the great missionaries that conquered hearts for Christ? What procedures did they follow in bringing the Light of Christ to others?

4. One way to learn about a religion is to learn about its founder. If someone wants to understand the Christian Faith, he must obviously study the life and teachings of Jesus Christ just as he would have to study about Buddha in order to learn about Buddhism. What has learning about the life of Mohammed taught you about Islam?

5.   What was life like for a non-Muslim in areas that had been conquered by Islam?

6.   What happened to Mohammed's followers after his death? How does this compare with the story of the early Christians?

The Wisdom of St. Gregory the Great

Destroy as few pagan temples as possible; only destroy their idols, sprinkle them with holy water, build altars and put relics in the buildings, so that, if the temples have been well built, you are simply changing their purpose, which was the cult of demons, in order to make a place where from henceforth the true God will be worshipped. Thus, the people, seeing that their places of worship have not been destroyed, will forget their errors and having attained knowledge of the true God, will come to worship Him in the very places where their ancestors assembled ... There is no need to change their customs at festivals. Thus, on the feast of dedication or on the feasts of martyred saints whose relics have been placed in the church, they should build booths out of branches round the church as they used to round pagan temples, and celebrate the festival with religious banquets ... Allowing them to give outward expression to their joy in the same way, you will more easily lead them to know inner joy, for be assured that it is impossible to rid such deluded souls of all their misconceptions at once. You do not climb a mountain in leaps and bounds, but by taking it slowly.

– *Letters* XI, 56

D. Application

This question asks you to think about how the lessons of history apply to today—either to the Church, to society, or to you. After meditating on this question, spend time with God in prayer.

Since its beginnings in the seventh century, Islam has had a profound impact on the Church and Western civilization. Our modern world continues to feel its impact. Over the centuries, missionary efforts to Muslim nations have not borne much fruit. Why do you think that is the case? In what ways can you help spread the message of Gospel to Muslims today?

Dear Lord ...

EPIC

Missionaries & the Emperor – Part II

A. Establish the Context

"Go therefore and make disciples of all nations, baptizing them in the name of the Father and of the Son and of the Holy Spirit, teaching them to observe all that I have commanded you."

– Matthew 28:19-20

While Muslim forces rampage and overrun Christian lands, a new round of heresies seeking to redefine who Jesus is once again attacks the Church from within. Once more the Patriarch of Constantinople proposes a Christological teaching at odds with the Apostolic Faith. This time Jesus is presented as having only one will – a divine will. This heresy essentially denies the true humanity of Christ by proposing that he lacked a human will. Unfortunately, Pope Honorius fails to unequivocally denounce the heresy, and it spreads throughout the Church. The question is finally settled at the Third Council of Constantinople (681). A century later the East is racked by another heresy advocated by the emperor, who declares sacred images to be a form of idolatry. This "iconoclastic" battle rages for over fifty years consuming the political and ecclesiastical life of the Church in the East (it would also affect the West during the sixteenth century Protestant Revolt). Eventually, the Second Council of Nicaea (787), using the writings of St. John Damascene, defines the Catholic understanding of the use of sacred images, condemning the notion that such use constitutes idolatry.

> **St. Boniface chops down the "Thunder Oak" of Thor**
> A.D. 723
>
> **Campaign of Charlemagne against savage pagan Saxons**
> 30 years
>
> **Gap between last western Roman emperor and the crowning of Charlemagne**
> 324 years

Missionary efforts continue during this time period, as St. Boniface spreads the Gospel to the inner areas of modern-day Germany. St. Boniface is known for his courage among the pagan Germans and for establishing a beloved Christmas tradition. An able administrator and friend to the Franks, he reforms the Church in Gaul and helps solidify the Faith of the Eldest Daughter of the Church. His missionary work helps bring more than 100,000 new converts to the Faith before he is struck down, along with several companions, by a pagan's war axe in 754.

Pepin, son of Charles Martel and sole ruler of the Franks after ending the Merovingian dynasty, fights the Lombards in Italy, who have been threatening the papacy. Granted the title "Protector of the Pope," Pepin, in turn, grants the lands captured from the Lombards to the papacy forming the temporal possession (known as the Papal States) of the popes for the next thousand years. The son of Pepin will reestablish a sense of unity throughout Western Europe through the creation of the Holy Roman Empire. Charlemagne becomes the King of the Franks in 771 and begins a life-long pursuit of imperial expansion in order to spread the Gospel and promote peace and prosperity. Inheriting his father's title as Protector of the Pope, he pledges to always serve the Church. Rome is full of violence and brigands. The pope is beaten by a mob while processing through the streets of Rome. He seeks shelter in France at the court of Charlemagne. Charlemagne's troops escort the Holy Father back to Rome. The king arrives in the Eternal City to celebrate Christmas, and on the Feast of the Nativity of the King of kings, the King of the Franks is crowned Holy Roman Emperor by Pope Leo III. Although unable to learn how to write despite years of effort, the emperor is a great patron of education and the arts. He devotes much of his time and resources to establishing an imperial education system. He personally selects a brilliant clergyman from England, Alcuin, who benefits from the writing of Venerable Bede, to standardize curriculum throughout the Empire. Alcuin creates what became known as the liberal arts curriculum by focusing on seven main subjects (grammar, logic, and rhetoric—the *trivium*; and arithmetic, geometry, astronomy, and music— the *quadrivium*).

But empires can be fragile things, and soon after Charlemagne's death, his realms are rent asunder. Once again harsh winds buffet Europe as Viking raiders and Magyar horsemen ravage the coasts and the countryside. In the East, the Byzantines continue to create conflict and division by allowing Photius, a mere layman, to depose the rightful Patriarch of Constantinople. Without a strong defender, the papacy becomes a bauble for the powerful Italian factions to wrestle over. Popes are captured, beaten, and sometimes murdered, with some hatred even going beyond the grave, as the gruesome trial of the corpse of Pope Formosus proves. With weak governance from Rome, many priests and monks slide into the depths of immorality. The temptation to despair is overwhelming.

But in the darkest night, even one lonely candle burns bright. In 909 Duke William of Aquitaine and St. Berno found the Monastery of Cluny, and it is these monks who nurture the seeds planted by Charlemagne. St. Benedict's Rule, written so long ago, governs these hallowed halls, and from this monastery will spring forth saints, popes, and a renewal that will purify the Church throughout the next century. The miraculous success of Cluny sets the foundation for the reform of the entire Church.

B. Learn the Story

View Track 7, *Missionaries & the Emperor – Part II*, of the *Epic: A Journey through Church History* 20-Week Study DVD (or listen to the audio CD). Follow the presentation by referring to your *Epic* Church History Timeline Chart.

NOTES

C. Take a Deeper Look

Answering these questions will help you learn the story of the Church. If other questions come to mind write them down to discuss in the group.

1. France has traditionally been known as the "Eldest Daughter of the Church." Why?

2. Charlemagne is considered one of the most important figures in Western civilization. What have you learned about him? Who do you think was a more significant Christian ruler, Constantine or Charlemagne?

3. Many modern critics accuse Charlemagne of being a tyrant because he forced the Saxons to convert to the Christian Faith. Can you explain the actual circumstances surrounding this event? Do you agree with the critics? Why or why not?

4. The Photian Schism was yet another step along the path that eventually led to the Great Schism, in which the Eastern Church broke away from the Catholic Church. Can you explain what happened?

5. What was the heresy of Iconoclasm? Which Doctor of the Church was one of its chief opponents?

6. The ninth and ten centuries are often called the "Dark Ages." What happened in the Church and Europe during this time period to warrant such a title?

7. The founding of the monastery at Cluny is one of the most significant events in the history of the Church and Western civilization. Why was it important?

> ### *St. John Damascene on Sacred Images*
>
> Since the invisible God took on flesh, we may make images of Christ, who was visible and picture Him in all His activities, His birth, baptism, transfiguration, His sufferings and resurrection. The image is a memorial; just what words are to a listening ear. What a book is to those who can read, that an image is to those who cannot read. The image speaks to the sight as words to the ear; it brings us understanding.

D. Application

This question asks you to think about how the lessons of history apply to today—either to the Church, to society, or to you. After meditating on this question, spend time with God in prayer.

This time period clearly illustrates that the Catholic Church saved Western civilization. Through the dedicated studiousness of monks, thousands of ancient manuscripts and classics of literature were preserved. Charlemagne's emphasis on education and art not only saved but also built up the patrimony of Western civilization. Today, through art museums, libraries, and the Internet, we have access to more cultural riches of the past than any generation before us. In what ways have you endeavored to appreciate and learn the classics of Western civilization? How can you grow in your appreciation for the Catholic heritage that has been handed down to you?

Dear Lord ...

E. Wrap-up

Conclude your study of the Missionaries & the Emperor period and remember the main events by doing the following:

1. What is the color of this time period? How can you remember it?

2. What is the main theme of this period?

3. Write a one- or two-sentence summary of the Missionaries & the Emperor period in order to recall the main events of Church history during this time.

F. Further Reading

For those who want to pursue outside readings, here is a list of good books that cover this time period whose authors approach the subject of Church history and Western civilization from a Catholic worldview. This list is not exhaustive but is provided as a starting point. Happy reading!

Ali, Daniel and Spencer, Robert. *Inside Islam: A Guide for Catholics.* West Chester, PA: Ascension Press, 2003.
   A question-and-answer book that provides a wealth of information on the history and theology of Islam.

Belloc, Hilaire. *The Great Heresies.* Rockford, IL: TAN Books and Publishers, Inc., 1991. *Chapter 4 is devoted to Islam, which Belloc argues is actually a heresy of the Christian Faith and not a unique religion. This fascinating analysis, written sixty-three years before September 11, 2001, also predicts the eventual return of a strong and militant Islam.*

Benedict, St. *The Rule of St. Benedict.* New York: Image Books, 1975. The Rule *of the Father of Western Monasticism whose monks preserved the patrimony of Western civilization.*

Bostom, Andrew, MD. *The Legacy of Jihad: Islamic Holy War and the Fate of Non-Muslims.* Amherst, NY: Prometheus Books, 2005. *This book is a compilation of eyewitness accounts, taken from Muslim and non-Muslim sources alike, of the early conquests of Islam. While modern Muslim scholars may argue that the jihad is to be interpreted as an internal struggle, it is clear that the early Muslim warlords took the idea of Holy War quite literally.*

Carroll, Warren H. *The Building of Christendom.* Front Royal, VA: Christendom Press, 1985. *Volume 2 of a planned six-volume work on the history of Christendom. These volumes are a scholarly read but highly enlightening and entertaining. Chapters six through sixteen deal with this time period.*

Gregory of Tours, St. *The History of the Franks: Penguin Classics Edition.* New York: Penguin Books, 1974. *A fascinating look at the history of the "Eldest Daughter of the Church." St. Gregory offers a brief history of the world up to the conquest of Gaul by the Franks and then provides a narrative of the kingdom of the Franks to the late sixth century.*

The Song of Roland. Translated by Dorothy Sayers. New York: Penguin Books, 1957. *This poem is a legendary depiction of a battle between some of Charlemagne's forces and a Basque army in the Pyrenees. While both Roland and the battle are historical, the descriptions in the poem are dramatic exaggerations. However, this is certainly one of the jewels of Catholic literature, and it reveals the way in which the men who lived in the centuries immediately following his rule viewed Charlemagne.*

Spencer, Robert. *The Truth about Muhammad: Founder of the World's Most Intolerant Religion.* Washington, D.C.: Regnery Publishers, Inc., 2006. *A fascinating and well-documented look at Muhammad, his life, his beliefs, and his influence.*

EPIC

Crusaders & Scholars – Part I

A. Establish the Context

"The Lord is a warrior. The Lord is His name."

– Exodus 15:3

The light of Cluny shines bright as the fruits of its labors take hold in the Church with the advent of a series of reforming popes. The papacy is made strong again, just as it faces new challenges to its authority. Seeking to prevent secular influence, a pope is captured in battle by the Normans and dies in captivity, while his envoy to Constantinople unleashes events that continue to wound the Church. The Great Schism between the East and the West permanently mars the unity of the Church. It is one of the saddest and most avoidable episodes in Church history. An ecclesiastical event of epic proportions, the Great Schism will significantly influence the birth of the crusading movement.

Pope and secular ruler continue to clash as Pope St. Gregory VII defends papal primacy against the desires of the "Protector" of the Pope, the Holy Roman Emperor Henry IV. The "Investiture Controversy" settles on the main question of who appoints bishops—the pope or the ruler? Pope St. Gregory VII safeguards the Chair of Peter and demands penance from Henry IV, who dramatically begs forgiveness from the Holy Father as a barefoot penitent in the snow outside the castle of Canossa.

The full energy and might of Christendom is marshaled in an extraordinary manner with the arrival of the crusading movement. Harassed for centuries by Muslim forces, the Byzantine Empire suffers a devastating loss at the Battle of Manzikert (1071) at the hands of the ferocious Seljuk Turks. This is the event that sparks 700 years of crusading history. Weak and in desperate need of troops, the Byzantine emperor sends a distressing plea for help to the pope. He finds a sympathetic ear from Pope Bl. Urban II, who travels to France at the end of autumn to rally the men of the Eldest Daughter of the Church. Pope Urban II unleashes the crusading movement by pleading for the sons of Charles Martel, Pepin, and Charlemagne to liberate the city of the Savior, Jerusalem.

100,000 respond to Urban's call to liberate Jerusalem, of which 60,000 are fighting men

Cost to go on crusade 4 times annual income

Blessed Urban II (1088-1099)

Motivated by love of Christ and the salvation of their souls, the crusaders embark on their defensive war to recapture ancient Christian lands. They successfully besiege the ancient Christian city Nicaea and march towards Antioch winning a significant victory at Dorylaeum (modern day Turkey). After a brutal march through the summer heat, the crusaders arrive at the gates of Antioch in a desperate situation. While the crusade leaders debated military tactics, the rank and file suffered from disease and starvation. News reached the crusader camp that a large Muslim relief army was on its way to Antioch. The situation looked completely hopeless. However, one crusade leader (Bohemend) was able to bribe a Muslim guard to open the city gates to the Christian army. The next day the Muslim relief army arrived on the scene and the besiegers became the besieged. Once more faced with a seemingly hopeless situation, the crusaders morale is uplifted by a miraculous vision. Peter Bartholomew, a monk accompanying the crusade, has a vision of St. Andrew who tells him the location of the Holy Lance that pierced the side of Christ on Calvary. Although some were skeptical of the authenticity of the lance, the majority of crusaders considered its discovery another sign of God's protection. The crusaders then sallied forth from Antioch and defeated a superior Muslim force. The crusade had liberated two important and ancient Christian cities, but the goal of the expedition remained: Jerusalem.

B. Learn the Story

View Track 8, *Crusaders & Scholars* – Part I, of the *Epic: A Journey through Church History* 20-Week Study DVD (or listen to the audio CD). Follow the presentation by referring to your Epic Church History Timeline Chart.

NOTES

C. Take a Deeper Look

Answering these questions will help you learn the story of the Church. If other questions come to mind, write them down to discuss in the group.

1. The mid- to later-eleventh century was one of reform in the Church and papacy in particular. What reforms were instituted? By whom? Why was reform necessary?

2. The Great Schism of 1054 rent the Church of Christ asunder, a wound that, unfortunately, continues into our own times. What happened during this momentous event? How can this wound be healed?

3. Pope Bl. Urban II introduced a revolutionary idea into the life of Christendom at the end of the eleventh century. What was that idea? What did it lead to?

4. The preaching of the First Crusade drew an enormous response. Why do you think people went on crusade? What motivated them? If you had lived at the end of the eleventh century, what would have been your response?

5. The First Crusade was the one truly successful crusade. How did it succeed and why? The crusaders were certain God was with them while they marched to Jerusalem. What events transpired to solidify this certainty?

> ### *Bl. Pope Urban II – The Importance of Jerusalem and the First Crusade*
>
> Jerusalem is the navel of the world; the land is fruitful above others, like another paradise of delights. This the Redeemer of the human race has made illustrious by His advent, has beautified by residence, has consecrated by suffering, has redeemed by death, has glorified by burial. This royal city, therefore, situated at the center of the world, is now held captive by His enemies, and is in subjection to those who do not know God … She seeks therefore and desires to be liberated, and does not cease to implore you to come to her aid … Whoever, therefore, shall determine upon this holy pilgrimage and shall make his vow to God to that effect … shall wear the sign of the cross of the Lord on his forehead or on his breast. When truly having fulfilled his vow he wishes to return, let him place the cross on his back between his shoulders.
>
> – Robert the Monk, *Historia Hierosolymitana*

D. Application

This question asks you to think about how the lessons of history apply to today—either to the Church, society or to you. After meditating on this question, spend time with God in prayer.

The Crusades are one of the most misunderstood events in Western history. Many modern myths have been perpetuated for so long that it is difficult to separate fact from fiction in our minds—despite the recent scholarship that is at odds with the popular stories. What were you impressions of the crusades before listening to this presentation? Have they changed? If confronted by someone about the Crusades and the Church, how would you respond?

Dear Lord …

N O T E S

Crusaders & Scholars – Part II

A. Establish the Context

"If any man would come after me, let him deny himself and take up his cross and follow me."

– Mark 8:34

The crusaders arrive at the walls of Jerusalem in July 1099, three years after leaving Europe. Miraculous events accompanied the armed pilgrimage which led to the liberation of the Holy City on July 15, 1099. Their pilgrimage complete, the majority of the crusaders returned home. A few stay in the newly created Crusader States. Constantly short of manpower, the Crusader States struggle to defend a 600-mile frontier. A unique response to this deficit arrives with the creation of military orders—fighting men who make the temporary act of crusading a permanent way of life in religious community. These "warrior monks" form the backbone of Christian defense by manning and running important fortifications throughout Palestine and Syria. Despite the rise of the military orders, the crusaders will soon be faced with a united Muslim force that will cause the downfall of one of the Crusader States (Edessa) and lead to the Second Crusade.

The main military orders:
– Hospitallers
– Templars
– Teutonic Knights
– Knights of the Holy Sepulchre

The siege & sack of Constantinople:
"Never have so many been besieged by so few."
– Geoffrey Villehardouin

"An event [the sack] that can be explained but not justified."
– Regine Pernoud

Although disunited at the arrival of the initial crusaders, the Muslims find unifying leadership in Zengi and Nur-ed Din. The former captures the city of Edessa, seat of the first Crusader State, and the latter solidifies his power by controlling the strategic city of Damascus. The fall of Edessa elicits a response from Western Europe, as Pope Bl. Eugenius III calls the Second Crusade. An overwhelming response to the crusade is the result of one of the most influential men in Church history, St. Bernard of Clairvaux. St. Bernard and his brother Cistercians traveled throughout Europe exhorting warriors to go to the East in aid of their fellow Christians. Among the many who "take the cross" are the Holy Roman Emperor Conrad III and the King of France Louis VII. There are high hopes for such a high profile affair. Unfortunately, the armies do not coordinate their plans and are beset by military and logistical setbacks. Hampered by casualties, the crusaders forgo the liberation of Edessa in favor of a siege at Damascus. This decision proves fatal and the siege is lifted quickly and the crusaders return home, as failures unable to duplicate the success of the brothers in arms fifty years before in the First Crusade. The crusading movement continues as a more menacing force arises in the East —a force that will undo the success of the past.

It is almost a hundred years since the first crusaders (called "Franks," regardless of nationality, by the Muslims) arrived in the Holy Land. Over that time, the Christian presence in the Crusader States has grown, but it still suffers from a shortage of manpower. The once disunited Muslim community is on the verge of unification. One man has a vision to push the crusaders into the sea and reclaim the holy city of Jerusalem for Islam. This man is Saladin. Born an ethnic Kurd and Sunni Muslim in the town of Tikrit (in modern-day Iraq), Saladin first consolidates power in Egypt by overthrowing the Shiite Fatimid caliphate and placing Egypt under the authority of the Sunni Abbasid caliphate in Baghdad. He furthers his influence over the Muslim community in Syria by marching into Damascus. Now, for the first time, one Muslim ruler controls both the northern and southern Muslim areas. In a position of immense strength, Saladin turns his sights on the coastal regions and home of the

Christians. The Kingdom of Jerusalem at this time is in a very weakened position. King Baldwin IV, although brave and competent, is young and stricken with the dreadful disease of leprosy. Upon his death, court intrigue develops, and the monarchy falls to his sister, Sibylla, and her much disliked husband, Guy de Lusignan. Guy is incompetent and foolhardy. He allows a rouge lord, Reynald de Châtillon, to raid Muslim trade caravans, providing Saladin with an excuse to invade the kingdom.

Saladin marches his army to the city of Tiberias on the Sea of Galilee and besieges it. He enters the city, but the citadel holds, and the Christian force sends a request for aid to King Guy. The king assembles the largest Christian army in the kingdom's history, depleting the garrison forces in most major Christian cities in the process, and marches to Tiberias in relief. Unfortunately, the march is uphill and in the midst of a brutal July summer. Making a devastatingly bad tactical decision, Guy pushes his army onwards rather than resting. The crusaders are easily surrounded by Saladin's forces near the "Horns of Hattin" (twin mountain peaks near the town of Hattin). The crusaders are without water and food and the army's military effectiveness is severely degraded. Occupying the strategic high ground, the Muslim forces taunt their Christian enemies by pouring water out of cups and lighting fires to increase the heat and suffering of the Christians. On July 4, 1187, the Muslims open their assault, the crusaders fight bravely, but the effort is wasted, as the army is decimated. Saladin then marches throughout the Crusader States, easily capturing many major towns. He arrives at Jerusalem in October and lays siege to the Holy City. After a spirited defense, the Christians surrender and Saladin's victory is complete.

The news of the fall of Jerusalem and of the majority of the Crusader States sends shock waves throughout Europe. The pope calls another crusade, and the response is overwhelming. The three major monarchs of Europe – Holy Roman Emperor Frederick Barbarossa, Richard I of England, and Philip II of France – all take the cross and journey to the Holy Land. Unfortunately, success is fleeting, as Frederick drowns crossing a river in Anatolia and Philip's jealousy of Richard forces him to leave the crusade after one siege. Richard continues the fight against Saladin but is not able to recapture the Holy City. Faced with political troubles at home, he enters into a peace treaty with Saladin and returns to England.

The crusading movement is buoyed by the election of Pope Innocent III, who calls forth another crusade to the East. The leaders of the Fourth Crusade decide to take the sea route to the Holy Land, and in need of transport, they enter into a contract with the Venetians. The crusade leaders grossly overestimate the number of troops who volunteer and are unable to meet their terms of the deal. Greatly upset, the Venetians demand that the crusaders help them conquer a Christian city as payment. Although strictly forbidden by the pope from joining that campaign, the majority of the crusaders participate, and the city falls. While the crusaders are encamped, a strange visitor from the East arrives with promises of gold and assistance in the crusade in exchange for the crusaders' help. They are asked to ensure the visitor's installment as Byzantine emperor. The crusaders decide to follow this young prince to the great city of Constantinople. The crusade is now woefully off course and out of control, and disaster results as the crusaders eventually sack the great city. The hope that the crusading movement might reunite East and West is lost.

B. Learn the Story

View Track 9, *Crusaders and Scholars – Part II*, of the *Epic: A Journey through Church History* 20-Week Study DVD (or listen to the audio CD). Follow the presentation by referring to your *Epic* Church History Timeline Chart.

N O T E S

C. Take a Deeper Look

Answering these questions will help you learn the story of the Church. If other questions come to mind write them down to discuss in the group.

1. Many modern myths surround the crusades including the "massacre of Jerusalem," during which it is alleged that the crusaders massacred all the inhabitants of the city upon its liberation. The story goes that so much blood was spilled the crusaders waded through it up to their knees. What is the true story of the liberation of Jerusalem?

2. One historian has remarked, "The Second Crusade was born by papal pronouncement, but it drew breath from the words of Bernard of Clairvaux." Who was St. Bernard, and what role did he play in the Second Crusade?

3. Although hopes were high, the Second Crusade was not as successful as the First. What happened on this crusade? Who were the main participants? Why did it fail?

4. The 2005 film *Kingdom of Heaven* (directed by Ridley Scott; starring Orlando Bloom, Jeremy Irons, and Liam Neeson) purports to tell the story of the Kingdom of Jerusalem right before the Third Crusade. Have you seen this movie? If so, share your thoughts on it. Are the historical events portrayed accurately?

5. The Third Crusade is probably the most well-known crusade. It is a dramatic story with larger-than-life characters. Who were the main actors in this great story? What happened during this crusade? Was it successful?

6. Pope Innocent III was one of the most influential popes in Church history. How did Innocent influence the Church and Western civilization?

7. One historian has remarked that the "conquest of Constantinople is one of those events that can be explained but not justified." Explain what happened during the Fourth Crusade. How has it affected the Church?

8. The Fifth Crusade was on the verge of great success when it ended in bitter defeat. Why did this crusade fail? A very important visitor arrived in the crusader camp. Who and why was he there?

Pope Innocent III's Letter to the Crusaders Who Sacked Constantinople

You rashly violated the purity of your vows; and turning your arms not against the Saracens but against Christians, you applied yourselves not to the recovery of Jerusalem, but to seize Constantinople, preferring earthly to heavenly riches … These "soldiers of Christ" who should have turned their swords against the infidel have steeped them in Christian blood, sparing neither religion, nor age, nor sex … They stripped the altars of silver, violated the sanctuaries, robbed icons and crosses and relics … The Latins have given example only of perversity and works of darkness. No wonder the Greeks call them dogs!

– As quoted in Warren H. Carroll, *The Glory of Christendom*

D. Application

This question asks you to think about how the lessons of history apply to today—either to the Church, to society, or to you. After meditating on this question, spend time with God in prayer.

Western Crusaders, against the explicit orders of Pope Innocent III, sacked the great imperial city of Constantinople in 1204. This one event has negatively shaped East/West relations for the last 800 years. Despite the effects of Pope John Paul II and Pope Benedict XVI, the Church remains disunited. In what ways can you help bring about a level of respect and understanding between East and West? Why should the Church and individual Catholics work for reunification?

Dear Lord …

EPIC

Crusaders & Scholars – Part III

A. Establish the Context

"I do not seek to understand so that I may believe, but I believe in order that I may understand. For this too I believe, that unless I first believe, I shall not understand."

– St. Anselm of Canterbury

The failure of the Fifth Crusade does not dampen the spirit of the crusading movement as Frederick II, Holy Roman Emperor, and King St. Louis IX of France lead the last crusades to the Holy Land. Known as the "Crusader without Faith," Frederick II lives a troublesome life. Raised as a ward of the Church at the papal court of Pope Innocent III, Frederick spends most of his life at odds with the papacy. He eventually fulfills his crusader vow, although excommunicated at the time, by traveling to Jerusalem, where he enters into a treaty with the Muslims, which grants Christian control of the Holy City for ten years. Frederick's infidelity is in sharp contrast to the holiness of King St. Louis IX.

St. Louis IX, known as the "Perfect Crusader," was an extraordinarily devout Christian and a loving husband and father. He truly believed in the righteousness of the crusading movement and spent large amounts of the royal revenue on two crusades to the East. His first crusade was almost a repeat of the Fifth Crusade to Egypt. Initially, St. Louis' adventure met with great success, but as he pushed inland, disaster struck. Muslim forces surrounded his army, and he was compelled to surrender. He spent a month in captivity before his ransom was paid. Although most of his men elected to return home to France, St. Louis stayed in the Holy Land for the next four years to rebuild the defenses and strengthen the kingdom. He returned to the East fifteen years later with another adventure to North Africa. Unfortunately, the crusade was over before it began. Disease swept through the crusader camp, killing St. Louis' second son, the papal legate, and many others. St. Louis himself contracted the illness and died mouthing the words, "Jerusalem, Jerusalem." The Perfect Crusader had given his all for the glory of God and His Church.

Establishment of Orders of Friars Minor *(the Franciscans)* 1210

Establishment of Order of Preachers *(the Dominicans)* 1216

The Seraphic Doctor St. Bonaventure

The Angelic Doctor St. Thomas Aquinas

There was trouble in southern France. A dangerous heresy arose that consumed the nobility and threatened the existence of the Church. Borrowing teachings from the Gnostics of old, the Albigensians (also known as the Cathars) once again preached that all matter was evil and only the spirit was good. These heretics set up a counter-church and, through their fasting and penances, presented the aura of holiness, which attracted many followers. The Church initially responded by sending preachers and envoys to the nobility to stir them into action against the dangerous Albigensians; however, this proved futile. A crusade was launched and under the direction of Simon de Montfort, who made great gains in conquering territory held by the heretics. Armed military force as a solution would not prove lasting. Instead, the Albigensian heresy was defeated and peace, order, and unity were restored through the efforts of the Dominicans and the medieval inquisitors.

This time period closes with great advances in the field of education. The universities, all initially established by the Church, are witness to the formation of the scholastic method of learning and the integration of theology, philosophy, and Sacred Scripture. St. Anselm of Canterbury begins this integration with his writings on why God became man and proving the existence of God. He roots intellectual learning and knowledge in the Faith by emphasizing that belief is necessary for understanding, not understanding in order to believe. His thoughts are expanded by some of the greatest minds in the history of Western civilization – men like St. Bonaventure, Peter Lombard, and St. Thomas Aquinas. These men provide not only the Church but also the whole world with an important patrimony in the field of intellectual and educational pursuits.

B. Learn the Story

Watch Track 10, *Crusaders and Scholars – Part III,* of the *Epic: A Journey through Church History* 20-Week Study DVD (or listen to the audio CD). Follow the presentation by referring to your *Epic* Church History Timeline Chart.

NOTES

C. Take a Deeper Look

Answering these questions will help you learn the story of the Church. If other questions come to mind, write them down to discuss in the group.

1. The relationship between Church and state has, at times, been quite tenuous. During this time period, England became the battleground between Church and state. What happened? How was the conflict resolved?

2. The history of the Church and of Western civilization was profoundly influenced by the arrival of Sts. Francis and Dominic. Who were these holy men? What impact did they have on the Church and the world? Who is your favorite and why?

3. One historian calls Frederick II "the Crusader without Faith." Who was Frederick II? What was his relationship with the Church?

4. In contrast to Frederick II, King St. Louis IX of France is called the "Perfect Crusader." Who was St. Louis IX? Why is he considered the "perfect crusader"?

5. What is heresy? What are its effects on the Church and society?

6. The Church launched a crusade against the Albigensian heretics in southern France in the thirteenth century. What were the beliefs of the Albigensians? How was the heresy eradicated?

7. Like the Crusades, the "Inquisition" is one of the most misunderstood and maligned events in Church history. Explain the creation of the medieval inquisitors. Describe the procedures used by these inquisitors. Were they just?

8.   What is scholasticism? Who were the main proponents? What was its effect?

King St. Louis IX to His Troops Before Invading Egypt

My faithful friends, we shall be invincible as long as we are undivided in our love. It is surely with divine permission that we have been brought as far as this, to disembark in a powerfully protected land. Whatever can happen to us will be for our good. If we are conquered, we shall be martyrs; if we triumph, the glory of God and of France, and of all Christendom will be exalted. This is God's cause; we shall conquer for Christ's sake. He will triumph in us; He will give the glory, the honor, the blessing, not to us, but to His name.

—As quoted in Regine Pernoud, *The Crusaders*

D. Application

This question asks you to think about how the lessons of history apply to today – either to the Church, to society, or to you. After meditating on this question, spend time with God in prayer.

The Church responded to the heretics in southern France in a variety of ways. Preaching and even fighting were utilized with little success. It was only the process of the Inquisition that restored unity and peace to the Church and society. When confronted by those who believe differently from you, how do you respond? Share an experience in which you defended the Faith to a person who had great animosity to the Church. How can the events of Church history help us to defend the Faith when the time arrives?

Dear Lord …

E. Wrap-up

Conclude your study of the Crusaders and Scholars period and remember the main events by doing the following:

1.   What is the color of this time period? How can you remember it?

2.   What is the main theme of this period?

3.   Write a one- or two-sentence summary of the Crusaders and Scholars in order to recall the main events of Church history during this time.

F. Further Reading

For those who want to pursue outside readings, here is a list of good books that cover this time period, whose authors approach the subject of Church history and Western civilization from a Catholic worldview. This list is not exhaustive but is provided as a starting point. Happy reading!

Belloc, Hilaire. *The Crusades – The World's Debate.* Rockford, IL: TAN Books and Publishers, Inc., 1992. *A military analysis of the Crusades. Belloc spends the most time on the First Crusade and ends with the defeat at Hattin in 1187. An insightful and thought-provoking work.*

Karsh, Efraim. *Islamic Imperialism: A History.* New Haven and London CT: Yale University Press, 2006. *A secular historian traces the rise of Mohammed and the history of Islam to the present day. Focus is on the imperialistic ambitions (present from the beginning) of Islam. The chapter on the crusaders does not reflect current scholarship but, overall, a well-done and engaging narrative.*

Madden, Thomas F. *The New Concise History of the Crusades – Updated Edition.* New York: Rowman & Littlefield Publishers, Inc., 2005. *The best overview of the crusades. Madden provides significant detail in a very readable work covering all eight traditionally numbered crusades as well as a discussion of the crusades outside of the Holy Land. This work ends with a fascinating discussion of the effects of the crusades on the current situation between Islam and the West.*

Pernoud, Regine. *The Crusaders: The Struggle for the Holy Land.* San Francisco: Ignatius Press, 2003. *Pernoud traces the history of the crusades by focusing on the men and women who participated in the movement. An enjoyable and educational book.*

_____. *Those Terrible Middle Ages! Debunking the Myths.* San Francisco: Ignatius Press, 2000. *A classic on illustrating the modern prejudice against the medieval world. Pernoud debunks the many modern myths through interesting topical studies.*

Peters, Edward. *Inquisition.* Berkeley and Los Angeles: University of California Press, 1988. *A thoroughly scholarly work that debunks the myths surrounding the Inquisition. A must-read for anyone seeking to understand the truth of the Inquisition and the context explaining its development and existence.*

Riley-Smith, Jonathan. *What Were the Crusades?* 3rd ed. San Francisco: Ignatius Press, 2002. *A short work from one of the most renowned crusade historians. In this book, Riley-Smith provides a sketch of the crusades with an emphasis on illustrating the characteristics of the movement.*

Strayer, Joseph R. *The Albigensian Crusades.* Ann Arbor, MI: The University of Michigan Press, 1992. *An outstanding overview of the political, social, and economic situation in southern France at the beginning of the thirteenth century. Strayer sheds light on why the Albigensian heresy arose and took root. He provides great detail on Albigensian belief and the crusade launched to restore unity.*

Walsh, William Thomas. *Characters of the Inquisition.* Rockford, IL.: TAN Books and Publishers, 1987 (Reprint). *Beginning with the Old Testament, extending through the medieval Inquisition and concluding with the Spanish Inquisition, Msgr. Walsh examines the chief characters in this history of the Inquisition. A delightful and informative read of the people involved in one of the most fascinating events of history.*

Weak Leaders & Schism – Part I

A. Establish the Context

"Seek first his Kingdom and his righteousness."

– Matthew 6:33

In seeking the riches of this world, men's hearts have grown cold. Within the mounting desires for wealth and power brews a tempest that can shatter Christendom, and it falls upon the papacy to hold back this rising storm. Alas, this period proves that the hearts of popes are not invulnerable to temptation.

The monarchs of Europe seek always to increase their might, and as King Philip IV (known as "the Fair" because of his complexion) of France begins taxing the clergy and trampling on the Church's independence, Pope Boniface VIII rebukes him with great vigor. Having already alienated himself from the other two great rulers of Christendom, the King of England and the Holy Roman Emperor, Boniface has no one to defend him from King Philip's fiery response. Philip's chief advisor and a group of armed men boldly attack Boniface, who dies only a month after his rescue by armed townsmen. King Philip ensures that the next pope, Clement V, sees things in a "French" way. So, at the whim of the French King, the powerful military religious order of the Templars is suppressed, and, in 1309, the pope moves his residence to Avignon. The nations begin to see the pope as the servant of the French rather than as the Vicar of Christ, and it is not until seventy-two years later that St. Catherine of Siena, a poor, humble, yet poignantly direct girl, is able to bring the Pope back to Rome.

The bulls of Boniface VIII:
– *Clericis laicos*
– *Ausculta fili*
– *Unam sanctam*

Popes in Avignon
73 years

23 million
(or 31% of the population of Europe)
dies from plague

Meanwhile, the Black Death shakes its horrid head and devours nearly a third of the population of Europe. In some cities, the mortality rate reaches as high as fifty percent with 400 people dying every day. Fear of death overrules love as husband abandons wife and mother abandons child; but the Church bears the worst wounds, as thousands of holy priests and religious give their lives tending the sick.

A year and a half after the papacy returns to Rome an even greater scandal rocks the Church. Chafing under the harsh treatment of Pope Urban VI, the college of cardinals, still dominated by Frenchmen, decides it was forced by the Roman mob into electing an Italian as pope. Foolishly, the cardinals attempt to go back on their first choice by electing a new "pope." The Great Western Schism has arrived, and it affects the Church for a generation, causing great scandal and a decrease in respect for the Church, the Faith, and the papacy in particular. In an attempt to heal the schism, some cardinals, theologians, and scholars make the situation worse by electing a third "pope." The monarchs of Europe leap into this bizarre circus, jockeying behind the papal claimant who best suits their needs. The heresy of conciliarism is born in an attempt to place more authority in the hands of ecumenical councils at the expense of the papacy. The scandalous Great Western Schism finally ends at the sixteenth ecumenical council in the imperial city of Constance (in modern day Switzerland). Pope Gregory XII declares the council and its act legitimate and then resigns for the good of the Church. The two antipopes are deposed, and Martin V is elected, restoring unity to Christendom. But the effect of schism and the long absence in Avignon severely weakens the authority of the papacy right before the time it is needed most.

B. Learn the Story

View Track 11, *Weak Leaders & Schism – Part I,* of the *Epic: A Journey through Church History* 20-Week Study DVD (or listen to the audio CD). Follow the presentation by referring to your *Epic* Church History Timeline Chart.

NOTES

C. Take a Deeper Look

Answering these questions will help you learn the story of the Church. If other questions come to mind write them down to discuss in the group.

1. Who was St. Celestine V, and what role did he play in the epic story of the Church?

2. Pope Boniface VIII is a controversial figure in Church history. Many historians see his papacy in a negative light, believing he is responsible for the weakening of the papacy and the rise of nationalism. Others believe he was a pope who had good intentions but his uncharitable and undiplomatic demeanor caused his ineffectiveness. Who was Boniface VIII? With whom did he quarrel? What is your judgment of his papacy?

3. For seventy-two years the pope lived in Avignon. What led to this relocation of the papacy? What brought the pope back to Rome?

4. How did people react to the Black Death? What were some of its long-term effects?

5. The Great Western Schism is perhaps one of the most confusing events in papal history. What caused the schism? Who were the true popes? How was the schism resolved?

6. What was the heresy of conciliarism?

The Black Death

The mortality in Siena began in May. It was a cruel and horrible thing; and I do not know where to begin to tell of the cruelty and the pitiless ways. Indeed, one who did not see such horror can be called blessed. And the victims died almost immediately. They would swell beneath the armpits and in their groins and fall over while talking. Father abandoned child, wife husband, one brother another; for this illness seemed to strike through breath and sight. And so they died. And none could be found to bury the dead for money or friendship. And in many places in Siena great pits were dug and piled deep with the multitude of dead. And they died by the hundreds, both day and night, and all were thrown in those ditches and covered with earth. And I, Agnolo di Tura, called the Fat, buried my five children with my own hands.

– As quoted in Warren H. Carroll, *The Glory of Christendom*

D. Application

This question asks you to think about how the lessons of history apply to today – either to the Church, to society, or to you. After meditating on this question, spend time with God in prayer.

During this time period, the Black Death ravaged Europe, killing men, women, and children by the thousands. Despite the great risk to their own lives, priests and religious rushed to bring the comfort of Christ to the sick. We must approach all things with the virtue of prudence, but there are times when we are called to take a chance or even make some sacrifices. Are you willing to sacrifice your own welfare to bring Christ to those in need? How have you helped those who are ill and in need of care? Do you visit the sick to lift their spirits?

Dear Lord …

Weak Leaders & Schism – Part II

A. Establish the Context

"And I tell you, you are Peter, and on this rock I will build my church, and the powers of death shall not prevail against it."

– Matthew 16:18

Heresy never sleeps, and once again it enters the stage to play a leading role in the drama of the Church. The main actors in this scene are Jan Hus and John Wyclif, who enter the stage preaching a "new Gospel" that rejects the Sacraments, denies the rights of the Church, abolishes the power of the pope, and lauds Sacred Scripture as the ultimate and only authoritative source of God's Divine Revelation. These "proto-Protestants" are finally stopped, but their seeds have already been sown. The execution of Jan Hus in 1415 ignites a conflict that foreshadows the revolution that is to come, and thousands of lives are lost before order can be restored.

In France, another war winds slowly toward its conclusion, and the English rejoice at their inevitable victory. They have little to fear from the penniless and pitiful Prince Charles, who is preparing to flee his own country. God chooses another peasant girl to humble the great. St. Joan of Arc, the poor, illiterate daughter of a simple farmer, steps forward to defend France, taking charge of an army at the age of seventeen. The Maid of Orleans lifts an unbreakable English siege, routs the enemy at every turn, and leads Prince Charles through miles of hostile territory to be crowned King of France at the Cathedral in Reims. She single-handedly reverses the course of the Hundred Years War, bringing peace and independence to the "Eldest Daughter of the Church." Sadly, this holy girl is captured, sold, condemned, and burned at the stake by her own countrymen who, for promises of wealth and power, gleefully collaborate with the English. King Charles VII, who owes his very crown to the Maid, does not lift a finger to save her.

How the Muslims Captured Constantinople– Urban's cannon:
– 27' long; 8" muzzle
– required 60 oxen & 700 men to move
– fired 1,200 lbs. solid shot

In the East, Islam crashes once again against the gates of the Byzantine Empire, and this time the flood cannot be stopped. Constantinople, believed to be an impenetrable fortress, falls before the Turks in 1453. St. Sophia, the largest Church in all Christendom, built by Justinian the Great in the sixth century, becomes a mosque, as Christians are slaughtered or enslaved by the thousands. Shock waves ripple throughout Europe, and Pope Nicholas V calls for a new crusade. The call goes unheeded. But as Islam gains ground in the East it is finally defeated in the West. After 770 years, the Spanish *Reconquista* concludes, and the Iberian Peninsula is once again in the hands of the Church. Queen Isabel reigns, and this strong, pious woman makes Spain one of the leading powers of Europe for the next 150 years. She commissions Christopher Columbus, expert sailor and devout Catholic, to weigh anchor in 1492, and to the surprise of many, he discovers something much greater than a new trade route to the Indies. Desirous of social, political, and religious unity, Isabel and Fernando establish the Spanish Inquisition, which ensures Spain's freedom from the bloody religious wars of the fifteenth and sixteenth centuries.

Back in Rome, wealth has glutted the Chair of Peter; a long line of men, known as the Renaissance popes, usher in a new age of learning and splendor. They commission some of the greatest artists of all time, such as Michelangelo, Raphael, and Leonardo Da Vinci, to create works of unparalleled beauty. But the price of this great art is a culture of decadence, and the Renaissance popes behave more as temporal princes than as holy priests. No one, however, can compare to Rodrigo Borgia, the infamous Pope Alexander VI, who shamelessly besmirches the papacy with a life of lust and greed.

It is a black and selfish time, and men's hearts have grown cold. The breaking of Christendom is close at hand.

B. Learn the Story

View Track 12, *Weak Leaders & Schism – Part II,* of the *Epic: A Journey through Church History* 20-Week Study DVD (or listen to the audio CD). Follow the presentation by referring to your *Epic* Church History Timeline Chart.

NOTES

C. Take a Deeper Look

Answering these questions will help you learn the story of the Church. If other questions come to mind, write them down to discuss in the group.

1. The Council of Constance (1414–1418) was one of the most important ecumenical councils in Church history. What happened at this council?

2. Who were John Wyclif and Jan Hus? What were some of their teachings?

3. Joan of Arc is one of the most captivating characters in all of Church history, but many modern critics and filmmakers paint her in an unfavorable light. What do you know about her story? Can you think of any myths about her? How can you defend her from these modern myths?

4. The fall of Constantinople shocked Christendom, and yet no one answered the pope's call for a new crusade. How do you explain this lackluster response?

5. What are some of the embarrassing facts about Alexander VI? A non-Catholic may cite these as reasons why the Catholic Church cannot be the one, true Church. How would you respond?

6. Explain the differences between the Spanish Inquisition and the medieval inquisitors? What are some of the widely accepted myths about the Spanish Inquisition? Can you explain the real story of the Spanish Inquisition?

7. Who was Savonarola?

The Rehabilitation of St. Joan of Arc by Pope Calixtus III

We say, pronounce, decree, and declare the said trial and sentence to be contaminated with fraud, calumny, wickedness, contradictions, and manifest errors of fact and law, and together with the abjuration, the execution, and all their consequences, to have been and to be null, without value or effect … We proclaim that Joan … did not contract any taint of infamy, and that she shall be and is washed clean.

– As quoted in Warren H. Carroll, *The Glory of Christendom*

D. Application

This question asks you to think about how the lessons of history apply to today – either to the Church, to society, or to you. After meditating on this question, spend time with God in prayer.

There are many spiritual benefits from studying Church history. Perhaps the greatest benefit is a deeper appreciation, love, and trust in the Holy Spirit. Reviewing the history of the Church and the papacy, especially during this time period, helps one to realize the Holy Spirit truly animates, guides, and preserves the Church in good and bad times. What is your relationship with the Holy Spirit? Do you pray specifically to the Holy Spirit? How can you deepen your understanding of the Third Person of the Holy Trinity?

Pray the Veni, Sancte Spiritus Prayer …

Come, Holy Spirit, fill the hearts of Thy faithful and enkindle in them the fire of Thy love. Send forth Thy Spirit and they shall be created. And Thou shalt renew the face of the earth.

Let us pray. O God, Who didst instruct the hearts of the faithful by the light of the Holy Spirit, grant us in the same Spirit to be truly wise, and ever to rejoice in His consolation. Through Christ our Lord. Amen.

E. Wrap-up

Conclude your study of the Weak Leaders & Schism period and remember the main events by doing the following:

1. What is the color of this time period? How can you remember it?

2. What is the main theme of this period?

3. Write a one- or two-sentence summary of the Weak Leaders & Schism period in order to recall the main events of Church history during this time.

F. Further Reading

For those who want to pursue outside readings, here is a list of good books that cover this time period whose authors approach the subject of Church history and Western civilization from a Catholic worldview. This list is not exhaustive but is provided as a starting point. Happy reading!

Alighieri, Dante. *The Divine Comedy: Inferno, Purgatorio, and Paradiso. Numerous translations are available. This is another crown jewel of Catholic literature. Constructing his work entirely around the theme of the Holy Trinity (from three books and three line verses to Hell, Purgatory, and Heaven being three levels of three circles each and a rhyme scheme in which each word rhymes three times), Dante weaves Catholic doctrine through a captivating story and masterful poetry.*

Chaucer, Geoffrey. *Canterbury Tales. Numerous editions exist, some with the original text and others with modern translations. Be sure to read an edition that includes the full "Parson's Tale," which is a long sermon that serves as the real conclusion to the book.*

Kamen, Henry. *The Spanish Inquisition: A Historical Revision.* New Haven and London: Yale University Press, 1997. *A thoroughly scholarly read about one of the most misunderstood institutions in history. Kamen presents an unbiased and well-researched account of the true Spanish Inquisition.*

Pernoud, Regine. *The Retrial of Joan of Arc.* San Francisco: Ignatius Press, 2007 (Reprint). *One of the best French historians offers a compiled edition of the manuscripts of St. Joan's retrial. Packed with the actual sworn testimony of St. Joan's friends, family, soldiers, and even enemies, this is an invaluable treasure that Ignatius Press has graciously reprinted.*

Madrid, Patrick. *Pope Fiction.* San Diego: Basilica Press, 1999. *An excellent little book that refutes numerous myths about the papacy, including common misunderstandings of the Great Western Schism and the scandal caused by bad popes.*

Twain, Mark. *Joan of Arc.* San Francisco: Ignatius Press, 1989. *Mark Twain was no friend of the Catholic Church, but even he fell in love with St. Joan of Arc. Calling her one of the most captivating human beings to ever live, he spent years researching this book and often remarked that he was most proud of it amongst all his other works.*

Walsh, William Thomas. *Characters of the Inquisition.* Rockford, IL: TAN Books and Publishers, 1987 (Reprint). *Beginning with the Old Testament, extending through the medieval Inquisition and concluding with the Spanish Inquisition, Msgr. Walsh examines the chief characters in this history of the Inquisition. A delightful and informative read of the people involved in one of the most fascinating events of history.*

Protestors & Defenders – Part I

A. Establish the Context

"For it is certain that a single monk must err if he stands against the opinion of all Christendom. Otherwise Christendom itself would have erred for more than a thousand years."

– Holy Roman Emperor Charles V about Martin Luther

In England, dramatic events unfold that foreshadow a struggle four hundred years later. The Church's independence is threatened by Henry II's insatiable thirst for power. Believing he has the Church in his pocket through the appointment of his friend and counselor, Thomas Becket, as Archbishop of Canterbury, Henry is surprised to meet the resilience of Becket's conversion and concern for the Church. The test of wills consumes England for six years and ends only with the dramatic murder of Becket in his own cathedral. Becket's martyrdom ensures the independence of the Church for the time being—until another Henry assumes the throne and demands that the Church grant him what he cannot have.

Luther nails 95 theses to Wittenburg church door
October 31, 1517

Peasants killed during revolt in Germany
130,000

Charles V
(1519-1558)

The Holy Spirit moves in mysterious ways, but He always gives the Church what she needs at the time she needs it. Never was this truer than with the arrival of the mendicant orders. The Franciscans and Dominicans, the first religious orders in the history of the Church to live through begging, are founded to serve the poor and preach the Faith. These orders are the culmination of the reform of the Church begun in the eleventh century. Their founders become some of the most well-known and beloved saints in the Church. The arrival of St. Francis and St. Dominic fills the Church with renewed spiritual energy, which she will need in the centuries to come.

The effects of poor leadership and lack of respect for the papacy become apparent as Christendom begins to break apart. The last of the Renaissance popes, Julius II and Leo X, continue to act more like secular princes than a universal shepherd. Although Julius safeguards the Papal States for the next 360 years and contributes to the greatness of Western civilization through outstandingly beautiful works of art (the Sistine Chapel ceiling, among others), the Church is still in desperate need of reform. His successor, Leo X, is incredibly self-indulgent and focused on satisfying his temporal appetites. An ecumenical council is called to address, among other items, the need for reform, and although the necessary decrees are passed, it is too little too late. Years of abuses and an unwillingness to pursue authentic reform until too late leave the Church vulnerable for attack. All that is needed is a spark, and the powder keg of dissent and revolt will ignite. The spark comes from Germany amidst the land of the Saxons, the fierce people resistant to conversion until the arrival of Charlemagne and his army. A lone Augustinian monk who professes Scripture at the local university provides the voice that shakes the Church to her very foundations and threatens her very existence. His focus is on the complete destruction of the Christian way of life since apostolic times. A reformer he is usually called, but he did not bring reform, but revolution.

Martin Luther enters the stage of the divine drama through the nailing of 95 theses to a church door in Wittenburg on October 31, 1517. A complicated man who has lived a severely troubled life, Luther begins the revolt that culminates in the breaking of Christendom and the shattering of Christian unity, the effects of which are still felt today. Initially upset at erroneous preaching concerning indulgences, Luther soon articulates more radical ideas, such as the desire to eradicate the Mass, the entire sacramental and priestly system, and the papacy, which he calls the Antichrist. The Church initially responds to Luther with letters and meetings. The great Cardinal Cajetan is sent to bring Luther back into the fold. Luther responds by insulting the writings of St. Thomas Aquinas (the cardinal was a Thomistic scholar) and remains steadfast in his revolt. Pope Leo X finally condemns Luther's teachings and orders him to submit to the obedience of the Church for the good of his soul. Luther responds by publicly burning the papal bull. He begins a furious writing campaign publishing three major treatises in 1520. These writings form the backbone of his thought and provide the blueprint for his attack against the Church. He advocates the destruction of the hierarchical structure of the Church; individual interpretation of Scripture; the elimination of holy days, pilgrimages, and clerical celibacy; and the establishment of a national German church separate from Rome. He describes the sacraments as the chief elements of the "Babylonian Captivity of the Church," implying that just as the Israelites were led into captivity by the Babylonians, so, too, has the Catholic Church led all Christians into captivity through the sacraments. Through the invention of printing by metal movable type, Luther's treatises are reproduced quickly and widely disseminated. Luther is a prolific writer, and his words flood Europe for the next twenty-five years. Luther's writings produce a wave of terrible violence throughout Germany as peasants, emboldened by Luther's revolutionary tone, rise up against the nobles. Protected from the Church and the Holy Roman Emperor by the nobles, Luther writes a scathing treatise against the peasants, urging the nobility to crush the rebellion through force of arms; more than 100,000 German peasants are slaughtered.

In the midst of the crisis in Germany, Pope Clement VII engages in the high-stakes game of temporal politics and loses. France and the Holy Roman Empire are at war over Milan, and the pope enters into a secret treaty with the French against the official Protector of the Pope, Charles V. Understandably upset, a large imperial army invades the Papal States and ultimately besieges Rome. Comprised mostly of Lutheran Germans, the imperial army breaks into the city, forcing Clement VII to take refuge in Castel Sant'Angelo. The imperial troops are uncontrollable as they sack the Eternal City for over a week; tens of thousands are killed, and sacrilege reigns supreme. The sack and destruction of the city come at a crucial time during Luther's revolt, handicapping Clement's ability to effectively deal with the situation.

Luther continues his revolt to the very end, publishing one last diatribe against the Church and the papacy before succumbing to a stroke at the age of sixty-six. The damage is done; the breaking of Christendom has begun, and the future is paved with more revolution and bloodshed. Luther provided the voice to the revolt against the Church, but the organizing of that revolt was left to another.

B. Learn the Story

View Track 13, *Protestors & Defenders – Part I,* of the *Epic: A Journey through Church History* 20-Week Study DVD (or listen to the audio CD). Follow the presentation by referring to your *Epic* Church History Timeline Chart.

N O T E S

C. Take a Deeper Look

Answering these questions will help you learn the story of the Church. If other questions come to mind, write them down to discuss in the group.

1. Pope Julius II is sometimes referred to as the "Warrior Pope." Who was this pope and in what ways did he contribute to Western civilization?

2. The sixteenth century event that shattered the unity of the Church is usually referred to as the Protestant Reformation. Was this event a Reformation or a Revolution? What's the difference?

3. Martin Luther criticized the authority of the papacy and the issuance of indulgences in his 95 theses. What is an indulgence? What was the real problem with indulgences at that time?

4. In 1520, Luther wrote three very important treatises that outlined his revolutionary plan. Name the three treatises. What were Luther's main teachings, and how do they contradict Catholic teaching?

5.   What happened at the Diet of Worms?

6.   Rome has been sacked numerous times in its history. The Sack of 1527 is particularly appalling because it came at the hands of imperial troops whose leader held the title, "Protector of the Pope." Why did this sack occur? What were its effects?

7.   Cardinal Cajetan met with Martin Luther and tried to avert a crisis and bring Luther back into the fold; he failed. What would you have said to Luther?

A Response to Martin Luther by Thomas Murner, O.F.M.

I must tear open my heart here in great bitterness, and speak with you briefly in plain German. And I will set aside all priestcraft, doctor's degrees, monkhood, monasticism, vows, oaths, promises and what not, by which I might seem laid under obligation, and will be simply a pious Christian. Well then, my father taught me from my youth up to show reverence to the Mass as a memorial of the sufferings of Christ Jesus our Lord, and thus all are taught who learn in the Holy Scriptures about our common Savior, Christ, that the Mass is a sacrifice, profitable for the living and the dead; it is our holy usage that has grown up with us since the time of the twelve apostles.

– As quoted in Janssen, *History of the German People at the Close of the Middle Ages*

D. Application

This question asks you to think about how the lessons of history apply to today—either to the Church, to society, or to you. After meditating on this question, spend time with God in prayer.

Martin Luther was a very complicated and conflicted man. He shared his personal beliefs with others in order to influence them to leave the Faith. His personal disagreement with certain teachings of the Church became public, which destroyed the unity of the Church and European society. One person's Faith (or lack thereof) can have huge ramifications for others. How do you influence others about the Catholic Church? Who has influenced you the most in your faith life? What can you do to ensure you provide a positive influence to others about the Catholic Faith?

Dear Lord ...

EPIC

Protestors & Defenders – Part II

A. Establish the Context

"For this reason a man shall leave his father and mother and be joined to his wife, and the two shall become one. So they are no longer two but one flesh. What therefore God has joined together, let no man put asunder."

– Matthew 19:5-6

What began in Germany continues in the idyllic city of Geneva. John Calvin, originally a follower of Protestant tenants, becomes the organizer of the entire Protestant movement. Calvin writes one of the most influential Protestant works, the *Institutes of the Christian Religion*, wherein he systematizes Protestant theology and develops his doctrine of the "elect" —those whom God predestines to salvation. Calvin moves to Geneva and established the first Christian theocratic state, where the personal faith lives of citizens are subject to government enforcement. Geneva becomes the first battle in the "war against joy," as the civil authorities outlaw all forms of entertainment. Life in Calvinistic Geneva is highly regulated, as pastors spend their time ensuring that women maintain proper hair length, do not wear jewelry, and name their children after Old Testament figures. Those who dissent from Calvin's teachings and regulations are imprisoned, exiled, or executed. Martin Luther was the voice of the Protestant revolt; John Calvin was the organizer. Through numerous letters, Calvin maintained contact with Protestant leaders throughout Europe, encouraging them in their revolt. He develops and organizes a Protestant church, creed, and way of life.

The "War Against Joy": Life in Calvin's Geneva Laws concerning:
– *color of clothes*
– *dancing*
– *singing*
– *staging theatrical plays*
– *wearing jewelry, lace, rouge*
– *length of women's hair*
– *names of children*

Geneva 1542-1546
– *58 executions*
– *73 exiles*
– *900 imprisonments*

In the midst of the Protestant revolt in Europe, a quiet, peaceful and grace-filled "revolution" is underway halfway around the world. Unlike the violent and bloody Protestant revolution, this is a revolution of the heart started by the appearance of a woman. The blood-soaked land of the former Aztec empire is in desperate need of conversion. Although it had been a decade since the end of the empire and missionaries were present in the land, conversions are few until the arrival of the Mother of God. She appears to St. Juan Diego in December 1531, and the land of Mexico would never be the same.

The revolt begun by Luther and advanced by Calvin had been confined to the continent of Europe, but in 1527, at the same time the city of Rome is being sacked by Charles V's imperial troops, the Faith in England is threatened by the romantic whims of her monarch. Henry VIII had received the title "Defender of the Faith" by the Pope for his response to the writing of Martin Luther. He is married to Catherine of Aragon, Charles V's aunt and daughter of the monarchs of Spain, Fernando and Isabel. Catherine gives him a daughter, Mary. But the temptations of the royal court become too much for Henry, who violates his wedding vows. One of his mistresses is not content to be just a mistress but set her sights on the crown. Youthful, prideful, and ambitious, Anne Boleyn leads Henry down the path of separation from the Catholic Church. What begins as a question of the validity of one marriage would end with the question of the faith of an island. England, through the whims of Henry VIII, would fall from the Faith and separate herself from the Church. Many holy men and women would give their lives for the Faith in England, providing hope for the future of a once proud Catholic nation.

The Church is in turmoil, Germany is wracked by constant confusion, France maintains the faith internally but supports Protestants externally, England is slipping away, and the dream that was Christendom is teetering at the edge of a precipice. Reform is desperately needed.

B. Learn the Story

View Track 14, *Protestors & Defenders – Part II,* of the *Epic: A Journey through Church History* 20-Week Study DVD (or listen to the audio CD). Follow the presentation by referring to your *Epic* Church History Timeline Chart.

NOTES

C. Take a Deeper Look

Answering these questions will help you learn the story of the Church. If other questions come to mind, write them down to discuss in the group.

1. Hilaire Belloc described John Calvin as the one "who began the war against joy." Who was John Calvin? Why did Belloc describe him that way?

2. What is the importance of Calvin and his teachings?

3. Evangelization efforts in Mexico before 1532, although vigorous, only produced 200,000 baptisms. In a four-year period from 1532–1536, 1.3 million people were baptized. What happened to affect such a significant change?

4. The Faith in England was lost over the desires of one man. What happened in England during this time period?

5. Many courageous saints refused to enter into schism when ordered by their government to reject the authority of the Pope. Who were some of these saints? What are their stories?

A Mother's Love

You must know and be very certain in your heart, my son, that I am truly the perpetual and perfect Virgin Mary, holy mother of the True God, through whom everything lives, the Creator and Master of Heaven and Earth. I wish and intensely desire that in this place my sanctuary be erected so that in it I may show and make known and give all my love, my compassion, my help and my protection to the people. I am your merciful mother, the mother all of you who live united in this land, and of all mankind, of all those who love me, of those who cry to me, of those who seek me, of those who have confidence in me. Here I will hear their weeping, their sorrow, and will remedy and alleviate their suffering, necessities and misfortunes … Am I not here? I who am your Mother, and is not my help a refuge? Am I not of your kind?

– The Blessed Virgin Mary to St. Juan Diego

D. Application

This question asks you to think about how the lessons of history apply to today—either to the Church, society or to you. After meditating on this question, spend time with God in prayer.

In his Gospel, St. John records the prayer of Jesus for his followers: "That they may all be one; even as you, Father, are in me, and I in you, that they also may be in us, so that the world may believe that you have sent me." This time period illustrates the fact that Christians have failed to live that prayer of Christ fully. Indeed, the last five hundred years of the Faith have been marked by the complete disintegration of unity among Western Christians. There are more than 33,000 different groupings of Christians in the world, whereas before 1517, there were only two major groups (Byzantines and Latins). What can we do to restore unity to the Church, as Jesus desired? How have I presented the Faith and the Church to my Protestant family members, friends, and co-workers? Do I pray for the restoration of Christian unity?

Dear Lord …

E. Wrap-up

Conclude your study of the Protestors & Defenders period and remember the main events by doing the following:

1. What is the color of this time period? How can you remember it?

2. What is the main theme of this period?

3. Write a one- or two-sentence summary of the Protestors & Defenders period in order to recall the main events of Church history during this time.

F. Further Reading

For those who want to pursue outside readings, here is a list of good books that cover this time period whose authors approach the subject of Church history and Western civilization from a Catholic worldview. This list is not exhaustive but is provided as a starting point. Happy reading!

Belloc, Hilaire. *Characters of the Reformation.* Rockford, IL: TAN Books and Publishers, Inc., 1992. *Character sketches of the main characters, male and female, in the drama of the Reformation.*

_____. *How the Reformation Happened.* Rockford, IL: TAN Books and Publishers, Inc., 1992. *Belloc's insightful analysis of one of the most important events in the history of Western Civilization. Belloc traces the careers of Luther and Calvin, and includes a discussion of what he terms "the English Accident." This work also covers the warfare that erupted in the sixteenth and seventeenth centuries, as well as a brief discussion of the Catholic response.*

Carroll, Warren H. *The Cleaving of Christendom.* Front Royal, VA: Christendom Press, 1985. *Volume 4 of a planned six-volume work on the history of Christendom. These volumes are a scholarly read but highly enlightening and entertaining.*

_____. *Our Lady of Guadalupe and the Conquest of Darkness.* Front Royal, VA: Christendom Press, 2004. *A history of the defeat of the Satanic Aztec Empire and the proclamation of the Gospel in the New World by Spain, along with the beuatiful story of the appearance of Our Lady to St. Juan Diego.*

Hughes, Philip. *A Popular History of the Reformation.* New York: Hanover House, 1957. *An excellent and highly readable book by a master Church historian. Hughes provides an overview of Christian belief prior to 1500, the practice of the Faith in 1500 as well as in-depth chapters on Luther, Calvin, England and the Council of Trent.*

Luther, Martin. *Ninety-Five Theses.* Philadelphia: Fortress Press, 1957. *This edition contains the 95 Theses translated into English with an informative introduction.*

_____. *Three Treatises.* Philadelphia: Fortress Press, 1966. *This volume contains Luther's three 1520 treatises,* Appeal to the Christian Nobility of the German Nation, On the Babylonian Captivity of the Church, *and* The Freedom of a Christian, *translated into English.*

The Catholic Reformation – Part I

A. Establish the Context

"Before the tribunal of God's mercy we, the shepherds, should make ourselves responsible for all the evils now burdening the flock of Christ."

– The Council Fathers of Trent

Persecution of Catholics in England
Over 700 known and documented cases of martyrdom under Elizabeth I

The Peace of Augsburg - 1555
cuius regio. eius religio
("his region, his religion")

England has been led into schism by the selfish and lustful desires of her monarch. The slope from schism to heresy is a slippery one and traveled by many throughout the history of the Church, and England is no different. England slides further from Rome as Archbishop Cranmer, the architect of English Protestantism, controls Henry's son, the young and sickly Edward VI. Cranmer, an indecisive man guided by political maneuverings, completes the break with Rome by abolishing the Mass and substituting a new liturgy of his own creation, with help and advice from John Calvin. It is now illegal to attend the Holy Sacrifice of the Mass on the once proud and fiercely Catholic island. Cranmer ensures that the separation from Rome is complete by changing the ritual for ordaining priests, removing all mention and understanding of the sacrificial nature of the priesthood, thus breaking the chain of apostolic succession and invalidating English orders in the future.

But all is not lost; there is hope, although just a glimmer. Edward dies and appoints Lady Jane Grey as his successor. Unpopular, she is removed from power after only nine days, and the crown is given to Mary Tudor, Henry and Catherine's daughter. Mary firmly believes that God had given her the throne in order to restore the true Faith to England. This is her determined and overarching focus throughout her brief five-year reign. She accomplishes this divine mandate, bringing the Faith back to England. However, there is a problem. Mary is thirty-seven years old, unmarried, and without an heir. If she were to die without an heir, the crown would pass to her Protestant half-sister, Elizabeth, and England would once again slip into schism and heresy. A marriage was desperately needed, and the Holy Roman Emperor proposed the perfect solution. Charles V suggests his son, Prince Philip of Spain, to be Mary's husband. Mary agrees, but the English people do not welcome the possibility of Spanish influence on their nation. Philip dislikes England and is not overly fond of Mary, despite her love for him. He leaves England, without providing England with a Catholic heir, to attend to matters in Spain. Mary's reign is marked by the execution of Protestant rebels who threaten the existence of her rule. These executions would earn Mary the moniker "Bloody Mary," despite the fact that the numbers affected pale in comparison to her better-known half-sister, Elizabeth.

Elizabeth's forty-five year reign, although tenuous at first, is motivated by a desire to eradicate the Catholic Faith and make England a world power. Through her trusted advisors, Elizabeth is able to accomplish both. Attending Mass, assisting Jesuits and other priests, and holding to the Catholic Faith are declared to be treasonous activities punishable by death. Not since Rome was there an empire where Catholics were persecuted in such numbers by the state. Despite these restrictions, the Faith survived in England through the brave missionary efforts of Jesuits and other priests, the heroic actions of ordinary English men and women, and the blood of the martyrs.

The effects of the Protestant Revolution were felt throughout Europe, as violence and warfare spread through the continent. Scotland became Protestant through the actions of John Knox. French Protestants threatened the monarchy and launched a series of civil wars over thirty-five years that almost resulted in the Faith's demise. Rebellion against the Spanish crown and the Catholic Church dominated events in the Netherlands. Germany, birthplace of the revolution, was mired in bloody conflicts for over a hundred years. Europe was in turmoil; the Church was in turmoil and in need of reform.

Reform finally came through one of the most important councils in Church history, the Council of Trent. Meeting sporadically over eighteen years, the Council gave the Church a doctrinally firm foundation and produced a reformation of clerical life. The decrees of Trent would be implemented by a saintly pope, a new religious order, and the actions of holy mystics, missionaries, and martyrs. The Catholic Reformation allowed the Church to purify and prepare herself for the troubled centuries ahead.

B. Learn the Story

View Track 15, *The Catholic Reformation – Part I,* of the *Epic: A Journey through Church History* 20-Week Study DVD (or listen to the audio CD). Follow the presentation by referring to your *Epic* Church History Timeline Chart.

NOTES

C. Take a Deeper Look

Answering these questions will help you learn the story of the Church. If other questions come to mind, write them down to discuss in the group.

1.   Archbishop Cranmer succeeded in moving England from schism to heresy. How did he accomplish this?

2.   Mary Tudor is often referred to as "Bloody Mary," while her half-sister, Elizabeth, is known as "Good Queen Bess." Are these labels accurate? Why or why not?

3.   Who were some of the English martyrs of this period?

4.   An agreement was reached in Germany in 1555 ending the Catholic–Protestant conflict. What was the name of that agreement? What were the details? Did it bring about lasting peace?

5. The Council of Trent is one of the most significant events in Church history. What happened at this Council? What were some of its teachings?

6. The Catholic Reformation emphasized three "D's." What were they and how were they implemented?

The Reason for the Spanish Armada

Onward, gentlemen, onward! Onward with joy and gladness; onward to our glorious, honorable, necessary, profitable and not difficult undertaking! Glorious to God, to His Church, to His saints, and to our country … Glorious to the saints, who have been persecuted, maltreated, insulted and burned … There also will await us the groans of countless imprisoned Catholics, the tears of widows who lost their husbands for the faith, the sobs of maidens who were forced to sacrifice their lives rather than destroy their souls, the tender children who, suckled on the poison of heresy, are doomed to perdition unless deliverance reaches them in time; and finally myriads of workers, citizens, knights, nobles, and clergymen, and all ranks of Catholics, who are oppressed and downtrodden by the heretics and are anxiously looking to us for their liberation … Let us live Christian lives, without offense towards our God; in brotherhood with our fellow soldiers and in obedience to our captains. Courage! Steadfastness! And Spanish bravery!

—Philip II to the men of the Armada – as quoted in David Howarth, *Voyage of the Armada*

D. Application

This question asks you to think about how the lessons of history apply to today – either to the Church, to society, or to you. After meditating on this question, spend time with God in prayer.

The Church was in serious need of reform. That reform came about through the Council of Trent and the actions of Pope St. Pius V, the Jesuits, and many holy men and women. In some ways, the Church is always in need of purification and reform, especially concerning the lives of her members. What areas of your life are in need of reform? In what ways can we make reparation for the sins of members of the Church? Why is this important?

Dear Lord …

EPIC

The Catholic Reformation – Part II

A. Establish the Context

*"The last knight of Europe takes weapons from the wall,
The last and lingering troubadour to whom the bird has sung,
That once went singing southward when all the world was young,
In that enormous silence, tiny and unafraid,
Comes up along a winding road the noise of the Crusade.
Strong gongs groaning as the guns boom far,
Don John of Austria is going to the war."*

– G. K. Chesterton, *Lepanto*

Dominican, Franciscan, and Jesuit chaplains were scattered throughout the fleet. Every man was given a rosary. The papal legate blessed the ships and the men. The Holy League fleet, 208 war galleys strong, under the command of Don Juan, left the harbor to seek out and destroy the menacing Muslim fleet bent on conquering Rome. The Ottoman Turks marauded through the Mediterranean throughout the sixteenth century. They conquered the island of Rhodes from the Hospitallers in 1522. Their war galleys were the scourges of the sea, raiding, pillaging, and capturing Christians for use as galley slaves. The Muslims also advanced over land, striking deadly blows in Hungary and besieging the gateway to Europe, Vienna. The very existence of Christendom was threatened. Selim II, sultan of the Ottoman Empire, prepared his forces for an attack on Rome itself, referring to the Eternal City as the "Red Apple" because he considered it ripe for the plucking. Pope St. Pius V sent letters to all the monarchs of Europe, seeking help against the Turks. Only the Spanish responded positively. Crafting a delicate alliance between Spain, Venice, and his own Papal States, St. Pius V formed the Holy League and placed Don Juan of Austria at the head of the largest Christian fleet ever assembled.

Order of Battle of Lepanto

*Christian fleet
208 galleys*

*Muslim fleet
300 galleys*

"This is not a moment for business; make haste to thank God, because our fleet this moment has won a victory over the Turks."
– St. Pius V

Don Juan knew the difficulty of his charge. He was sent to find and destroy the Muslim fleet. The illegitimate son of the Holy Roman Emperor, Charles V, was a mere twenty-four years old when the fate of Christian Europe was placed on his shoulders. Leading the Christian galleys to the Gulf of Lepanto, he engaged the enemy fleet on October 7, 1571. Although outnumbered, the Christian fleet aligned in the form of the cross, experienced a miraculous change of the wind at the crucial moment of the battle, and defeated the crescent-formed Muslim fleet, destroying and capturing more than 200 galleys to the loss of only twelve. Christendom was saved. In thanksgiving, the Dominican pope with a great devotion to Our Lady proclaimed October 7 as the Feast of Our Lady of Victory (later changed and still celebrated as the Feast of Our Lady of the Rosary).

The reform of the Church, spurred on by the decrees of Trent and the actions of Pope St. Pius V, was furthered through the lives of several great holy men and women. St. Teresa of Avila and St. John of the Cross undertook the reform of the Carmelite order, providing the Church with holy communities of men and women whose prayers uplifted and sanctified the Church. St. Charles Borromeo, the archbishop of Milan, provided an authentic witness of reform in his diocese, establishing seminaries and fostering holiness among his priests.

St. Philip Neri presented a life of holiness in the heart of the Church. The witness of his simple, holy life and his founding of the Oratorians gave Rome an example of holiness that attracted many priests and laity.

Holy men and women were sent throughout the world as missionaries to Protestant lands, the Far East, and the New World in order to invite those who had left the Church to return and to take the Gospel to places where it had never been preached before. Unfortunately, the colonies in the New World participated in the heinous sin against human dignity, slavery. The Church was not silent, as pronouncements from popes, as well as exhortations from hard-working and saintly missionaries, promoted the dignity of every human person and called for the abolition of the slave trade.

Jesuit missionaries braved severe conditions and ruthless Iroquois to bring the Good News of Christ to the inhabitants of North America. They witnessed among the peaceful Hurons in the regions of modern-day upstate New York and Quebec. St. Isaac Jogues was captured by Mohawks and brutally tortured, losing several of his fingers. He escaped and made his way back to France, where he requested to return to North America to continue his work. Captured once again, he was martyred for the Faith in a village nestled amidst the idyllic Mohawk Valley. His death was not in vain, for the "blood of the martyrs is the seed of Christians." Ten years after his martyrdom, a future saint of the Church was born in the same village, Kateri Tekakwitha.

The reform was producing results, and the Church had regained some of her lost respect and credibility when an event that would affect her for centuries occurred. A professor of mathematics at the University of Padua believed he could prove the theory initially proposed by Nicholas Copernicus, that the earth revolved around the sun. Although that was the scientific basis of Galileo's thought, there was something much more important at stake: the question of what explains reality—science, faith, or both. Galileo's real theory was the advancement of the notion that science alone explained reality. He attempted to answer a metaphysical question with a physical response, and this caused him to run afoul of Pope Urban VIII.

Less than fifty years after the Galileo affair, Christendom's existence was once more threatened by the Ottoman Turks who once more besieged the great city of Vienna. Polish forces under King Sobieski rescued the city on a date that should be among the most famous in history. Despite this miraculous rescue, the Church was faced in the next century with a more insidious enemy that very nearly destroys her.

B. Learn the Story

View Track 16, *The Catholic Reformation – Part II,* of the *Epic: A Journey through Church History* 20-Week Study DVD (or listen to the audio CD). Follow the presentation by referring to your *Epic* Church History Timeline Chart.

NOTES

C. Take a Deeper Look

Answering these questions will help you learn the story of the Church. If other questions come to mind, write them down to discuss in the group.

1. The decrees of a council need to be implemented for there to be any lasting change in the Church. Who implemented the decrees of Trent? How?

2. The Battle of Lepanto is one of the most significant events in the history of the Church. Why? What happened?

3. This time period is witness to several saints who contributed to the reform of the Church. Name several and discuss their role in the Catholic Reformation.

4. Critics often accuse the Church of remaining silent and even of advocating the slavery of indigenous people. Are these accusations accurate? How would you respond to someone who voiced these criticisms?

5. The French were very active in missionary work in North America during this time period. Who were some of the holy men and women who carried the Gospel to the New World?

6. What was the real issue between the Church and Galileo?

7. Many people cite the Galileo affair as evidence that the Church is against science. Is this an accurate viewpoint? What is the relationship between faith and reason?

Among the Hurons in North America

After earnestly praying to God we considered that it was his will, because the harvest of souls is riper here than else—whereas much because of my acquaintance with the people here and of the kindness they showed to me before, as because they are already half instructed in the Faith. As a matter of fact, we have baptized eight of them, of whom seven have in their baptismal innocence gone to heaven. The whole place is so well disposed that it is quite simply waiting for baptism. On such dispositions and foundations we hope, with God's grace, to build the Christian Church among these people ... Trusting in the goodness of God and not in our own strength or efforts, here is what we have done for the conversion of this race since our coming. First of all, we busied ourselves, studying the language which because of the complexity of its compound words seems endless. After that we are busied in visiting, pleading with, and instructing the sick, who are ... very numerous.

– Jean de Brébeuf, *The Huron Relation of 1635*

D. Application

This question asks you to think about how the lessons of history apply to today – either to the Church, to society, or to you. After meditating on this question, spend time with God in prayer.

Galileo attempted to answer metaphysical questions (e.g., What is truth? What is reality?) with physical answers. He believed and advocated that science is superior to and supplants faith. His underlying premise was that there is only one path to explaining the truth of reality—observation and reason; all other explanations are wrong. The Church countered Galileo by insisting on the complementarity of faith and reason. Both help to explain the world God created because both come from God. Pope John Paul II beautifully expressed the Church's teaching in this area in the introduction to his encyclical *Fides et Ratio*: "Faith and reason are like two wings on which the human spirit rises to the contemplation of truth; and God has placed in the human heart a desire to know the truth—in a word, to know himself—so that, by knowing and loving God, men and women may also come to the fullness of truth about themselves." Do you desire to know the truth? How do you go about that? How can we know the fullness of ourselves by knowing God? How do I see the relationship between faith and reason?

Dear Lord ...

E. Wrap-up

Conclude your study of the Catholic Reformation period and remember the main events by doing the following:

1. What is the color of this time period? How can you remember it?

2. What is the main theme of this period?

3. Write a one- or two-sentence summary of the Catholic Reformation period in order to recall the main events of Church history during this time.

F. Further Reading

For those who want to pursue outside readings, here is a list of good books that cover this time period whose authors approach the subject of Church history and Western civilization from a Catholic worldview. This list is not exhaustive but is provided as a starting point. Happy reading!

Beeching, Jack. *The Galleys at Lepanto.* New York: Charles Scribner's Sons, 1983. *A history of the Battle of Lepanto with an in-depth overview of the Muslim menace in the Mediterranean in the sixteenth century and the inner-workings of court life in Spain. Provides significant biographical information on Don Juan and Philip II.*

Brébeuf, Jean de. *The Huron Relation of 1635.* Midland, Ontario: Martyrs' Shrine, 1993. *The account of one of the North American martyrs among the Hurons, with an historical overview of the Jesuit missionary efforts in New France.*

Chesterton, G.K. *Lepanto – With Explanatory Notes and Commentary.* Edited by Dale Ahlquist. San Francisco: Ignatius Press, 2003. *The classic, yet almost forgotten, poem by Chesterton on the Battle of Lepanto. This edition contains several chapters that provide further background and insight into the battle. A bonus Chesterton essay on what would have happened had Don Juan and Mary Stuart (Queen of Scots) married is included.*

Daniel-Rops, Henri. *The Catholic Reformation.* 2 vols. Garden City, NY: Image Books, 1964. *An excellent work from a great Catholic historian. Daniel-Rops provides a compelling and entertaining narrative that traces the events and people of the Catholic Reformation.*

Macdougall, Angus J., ed. *Martyrs of New France.* Midland, Ontario: Martyrs' Shrine, 1992. *A collection of short chapters on the lives of several Jesuit martyrs of North America including a firsthand account by St. Isaac Jogues of the martyrdom of René Goupil.*

Rowland, Wade. *Galileo's Mistake: A New Look at the Epic Confrontation between Galileo and the Church.* New York: Arcade Publishing, 2001. *A fascinating book with a refreshing and objective look at the Galileo Affair. The author provides appropriate scientific background to help explain the story and intersperses his Galileo narrative with modern-day conversations between himself, a nun, and a skeptical friend.*

Stoye, John. *The Siege of Vienna: The Last Great Trial between Cross and Crescent.* New York: Pegasus Books, 2000. *Stoye describes the 1683 siege of Vienna with great detail and an insightful narrative. He concludes with a discussion of the importance of the Christian victory and how the event shaped (and continues to shape) the history of Western civilization.*

EPIC ✠

Revolutions & Modernism

A. Establish the Context

"Be sober, be watchful. Your adversary the devil prowls around like a roaring lion, seeking some one to devour."

– 1 Peter 5:8

"What is truth?" asked a Roman procurator of a Jewish carpenter many years ago. "You have no hope of knowing," answers the modern philosopher. In the name of reason and science, the "Enlightenment" gives rise to blinding arrogance, and oceans of doubt swell to fill the void created by men so proud that they think they can cut away the branch that holds them up without suffering the fall. It is a time when Europe rejects the drama of salvation history and spurns the organization that built up her own civilization. The effects of this "Enlightenment" are still felt today. Voltaire, a leader of this philosophical revolution, viciously bites the hand of his own master, devoting himself to suppressing the very Jesuit teachers who labored so hard to help him manifest his own brilliance. Faithless kings take up the cause, removing one of the last obstacles that stand between them and unlimited power. Pope Clement XIV, Christ's own vicar, pitifully submits to their will, and in 1773 the Jesuits, staunch soldiers of Christ, are suppressed.

Suppression of the Jesuits
1773-1814

**Fruits of the
French Revolution**
20,000 people guillotined

Modernism
"the synthesis of all heresies"
(St. Pius X)

In these turbulent times, the Church turns to her "Eldest Daughter," but King Louis XIV, epitome of the absolute monarch, will not bow to the Fisher of Men. Undoing Clovis' humble baptism centuries ago, France embraces Gallicanism (the subjection of the Church in France to the state) and tramples upon the pope's authority like a rebellious child. "Enlightened" thinking is taken to its logical conclusion when France, mired in the midst of a financial crisis, tears herself apart in a bloody reign of terror at the hands of revolutionary brigands. In the name of "Reason," every last shred of Catholic heritage is torn up by the roots. Any who oppose the new regime are traitors to the state. Bishops and priests must pledge allegiance to the Republic, but most of these loyal sons of the Church refuse. Loss of their parishes and diocese is their reward; it is soon followed by imprisonment and then gruesome death. The pious and merciful King Louis XVI and Marie Antoinette, who had labored hard for their people, are rewarded with the blood-caked blade of Madame Guillotine, and across the country the Church, the "infamous thing" that Voltaire so longed to destroy, is crushed.

The revolutionaries deface the most glorious buildings the world has ever known. The ancient monastery of Cluny is auctioned brick by brick, and the standard that St. Joan of Arc carried into battle is destroyed. The miraculous vial of chrism, used to anoint every French king since Clovis himself, is smashed against the stone steps at Reims. Men, women, children, nuns, and infants are slaughtered by the thousands as Reason is proclaimed the new god. In the Vendée, outraged peasants rise up to defend the Altar and the Throne, and battle by bloody battle they strive to end the persecutions until order is finally restored through the actions of one man: Napoleon Bonaparte. Napoleon invades Italy, taking the pope prisoner and in a matter of years all Europe trembles under his shadow. Recognizing the importance and influence of the Church among the people, he restores limited freedom to the Church. Napoleon's arrogance and the unified might of Europe defeat him, and he ends his days in exile.

Free from the French threat, Italy turns to her own affairs. "Unification" is her cry, and woe to the pope who now blocks her way. The Papal States, donated to the Church more than a thousand years earlier, are torn from Pope Bl. Pius IX's hands, and at last the loss of the papacy's temporal power is complete. Locked away in tiny Vatican City, though, the pope refuses to yield his spiritual authority. In 1854, he boldly issues the landmark decree *Ineffabilis Deus*, proclaiming the Blessed Virgin Mary's Immaculate Conception. Four years later, the Virgin Mary visits a poor French peasant girl and gives her own testimony to this Dogma of the Faith, and even today the healing waters of this humble grotto in Lourdes work the miracles of God.

But Satan still prowls. What began as philosophical doubt grows into a rejection of the Faith by attacking it from within. Prehistoric Man fell when Adam and Eve stole for themselves the knowledge of good and evil. Modern Man falls by eradicating any distinction between the two. Who decides right from wrong when all things can be right to someone? Who can judge what is beautiful when all things are beautiful to someone? Order is replaced by chaos, self-restraint by immorality, reason by emotion, hope by despair, and love by lust. There is only one "truth" that all men must accept: God does not exist. Modernism is the name of this hideous inversion, and its influence is felt within the Church herself.

Christ's Church is not idle. She battles these "revolutionary" ideas with Truth and Charity through the writings of Pope Bl. Pius IX and his calling of the first ecumenical council in 300 years. But the fruits of Modernism and the Enlightenment come to fruition in Germany, where a cultural war is waged against the Church. The Church does not back down and continues to call men to the Truth. The Holy Spirit guides the Church during these turbulent times of Revolution and Modernism, providing the Church with strong leaders and the world the example of saintly men and women: St. John Bosco embraces the poor children of Italy; St. Elizabeth Ann Seton founds the first parochial school in America; St. Frances Cabrini welcomes immigrants to the New World; St. Thérèse shows the world her Little Way. Finally, the steely Pope St. Pius X rallies the soldiers of Christ to stand strong against the evil that surrounds them. Satan's bonds have been loosed, and he is about to strike.

B. Learn the Story

View Track 17, *Revolutions & Modernism,* of the *Epic: A Journey through Church History* 20-Week Study DVD (or listen to the audio CD). Follow the presentation by referring to your *Epic* Church History Timeline Chart.

NOTES

C. Take a Deeper Look

Answering these questions will help you learn the story of the Church. If other questions come to mind, write them down to discuss in the group.

1.   How did the Enlightenment change philosophy? What was René Descartes' solution to the problem of doubt?

2. What motivated the suppression of the Jesuits? How was it achieved?

3. The French Revolution is one of the most awful events in modern history, but countless modern myths have obscured this reality. What were your thoughts on the French Revolution before you started this session of the *Epic* timeline? Has your opinion changed? What new facts did you learn that surprised you the most?

4. What is Modernism? Can you name some of its principal characteristics?

5. Who were some of the great popes that reigned during this time period? What were some of their achievements?

6. What were some of the issues the First Vatican Council was supposed to address? What major documents did it issue? Why was it cut short?

7. What was the *Kulturkampf*? Why was it instituted, and how was it defeated?

> ### *The Fruits of "Enlightened Thinking"*
>
> The entire drama of salvation history had disappeared as far as the Enlightenment was concerned. Man remained alone: alone as creator of his own history and his own civilization; alone as one who decides what is good and what is bad, as one who would exist and operate even if there were no God. If man can decide by himself, without God, what is good and what is bad, he can also determine that a group of people is to be annihilated."
>
> – John Paul II, *Memory and Identity*

D. Application

This question asks you to think about how the lessons of history apply to today—either to the Church, to society, or to you. After meditating on this question, spend time with God in prayer.

Despite the warnings of the popes, Modernism is still with us today. In modern Western culture, science always trumps faith, miracles are considered myths, Scripture is treated as a fairy tale, atheism is considered intellectual, morality is completely relative, and religion must be separated from the state. Where do you encounter Modernism in your own life? What can you do to fight this error?

Dear Lord …

E. Wrap-up

Conclude your study of the Revolutions & Modernism period and remember the main events by doing the following:

1. What is the color of this time period? How can you remember it?

2. What is the main theme of this period?

3. Write a one- or two-sentence summary of the Revolutions & Modernism period in order to recall the main events of Church history during this time.

F. Further Reading

For those who want to pursue outside readings, here is a list of good books that cover this time period whose authors approach the subject of Church history and Western civilization from a Catholic worldview. This list is not exhaustive but is provided as a starting point. Happy reading!

Carroll, Warren H. *The Revolution against Christendom.* Front Royal, VA: Christendom Press, 2005. *Volume 5 of a planned six-volume work. This volume presents a detailed narrative of the events of the French Revolution and its effect on the Church.*

De la Torre, Teodoro. *Popular History of Philosophy.* Houston: Lumen Christi Press, 1988. *A well-written history of philosophy stretching from ancient Greece to the twentieth century, including chapters on the important "Enlightenment" philosophers.*

John Paul II. *Memory and Identity: Conversations at the Dawn of a Millennium.* New York: Rizzoli, 2005. *The last book of Pope John Paul II. In this work, the late pontiff provides his insights on the European history and the politics of the modern world. He gives an excellent and insightful discussion on the Enlightenment and how it affected the Church and European society.*

Mioni, Anthony J., Jr. *The Popes Against Modern Errors: 16 Papal Documents.* Rockford, IL: TAN Books and Publishers, Inc., 1999. *An invaluable collection of decrees from Popes Leo XIII, Pius IX, and Pius X, among others.*

Newman, John Cardinal. *Apologia Pro Vita Sua.* Mineola, NY: Dover Publications, Inc., 2005 (Reprint). *This time period was witness to an English Catholic Renaissance. When the well known Anglican John Henry Newman converted to the Catholic Faith, he received much criticism, especially from a man named Charles Kingsley. This amazing defense of his conversion is only one of the many brilliant books Cardinal Newman contributed to the treasure trove of Catholic literature.*

St. Thérèse of Lisieux. *The Story of a Soul.* Translated by John Beevers. Garden City, NY: Image Books, 1957. *The autobiography of the great St. Thérèse of Lisieux, the Little Flower of the Child Jesus, whom Pope St. Pius X called "the greatest saint in modern times" and Pope John Paul II named a Doctor of the Church.*

Trochu, Francis. *Saint Bernadette Soubirous.* Translated by John Joyce, S.J. Rockford, IL: TAN Books and Publishers, Inc., 1985 (Reprint). *This biography of St. Bernadette features many great photographs of the saint and her surroundings.*

A World at War

A. Establish the Context

"And out came another horse, bright red; its rider was permitted to take peace from the earth, so that men should slay one another; and he was given a great sword."

– Revelation 6:4

The cold-blooded murder of one man, Archduke Franz Ferdinand of the Austro-Hungarian Empire, ushers in this satanic age of war. Austria declares war upon Serbia for the assassination of one of her most beloved sons, but Serbia does not fight alone. An international pact draws Russia to Serbia's defense, which motivates Germany to take action on behalf of her Austrian ally. Germany's ruthless offensive against France, however, storms through Belgium, an innocent bystander, and England quickly lunges to her defense. Through a well-woven web of treaties, all Europe is now ensnared in war. But war is not what it used to be. The industrial age gave birth to new wonders of death, and now hundreds of thousands of men are cut down in the jaws of merciless machine guns. Miles and miles of trenches fill with mud, poison, and blood while, from the safety of headquarters far removed from the front, generals sacrifice whole battalions to advance a few paltry yards. Pride blinds them to the horrors suffered by their men, and they continue to stubbornly order their men into the slaughter. Only two souls sue for peace. One is the weary Pope Benedict XV, his pleas drowned out by thundering artillery. The other is the Austrian Emperor Bl. Karl Hapsburg, a devout Catholic and saintly ruler who alone offers large concessions to end the war. Scorn and eventual banishment, through the Treaty of Versailles, are his rewards.

Casualties suffered by British Army on *first day* of the Battle of the Somme, 1916
60,000

"Anti-Semitism is inadmissible; spiritually, we are all Semites."
– Pius XI

Jews saved by actions of Pius XII and the Church during World War II
860,000

Amidst this carnage a divine plan for peace is delivered to three poor Portuguese children by the Mother of God herself. The Blessed Virgin Mary visits Jacinta, Francisco, and Lucia, confiding to them prophetic secrets and requests for all souls to pray the Rosary. Although many are skeptical, grace prevails, with 70,000 eyewitnesses beholding the breathtaking Miracle of the Sun on October 13, 1917. The Holy Virgin predicts the end of the First World War, as well as the coming of the Second. Casting her knowing eye towards Russia, Mary asks for this country to be consecrated especially to her Immaculate Heart lest evil should spread throughout the world. She knows what darkness lies ahead.

With millions upon millions dead or maimed, the horrendous war draws to an end. But for Russia it is too late, for the bright red banners of revolution are already flying. That revolution comes in 1917, as the Communists begin their bloody rise to power. The merciless and unstoppable Lenin steers this tidal wave, which seeks to destroy everything in the name of "the people." High on his agenda is the annihilation of the Christian Faith, whether Russian Orthodox or Catholic, and the sinister underlings riding in Lenin's wake, such as Trotsky and the ruthless Stalin, are happy to continue the persecutions after Lenin's death. They destroy thousands of churches and make hundreds of thousands of Catholics, including every Catholic bishop, simply "disappear."

No barrier, not even an entire ocean, can hold back Lenin's revolution. The full flowering of the anti-Catholic ideas planted in the Protestant Revolt and nurtured by the Enlightenment also come to the land of Mexico, evangelized long ago by the appearance of Our Lady. A socialist, anti-religious government is established. The state closes numerous Catholic churches, schools, hospitals, and orphanages, confiscates Church property, and forbids clergy to wear religious clothing in public. It is not long before thousands of the faithful are crowned with the glory of martyrdom. "Viva Cristo Rey" ("Long Live Christ the King!") rings out from the lips of Blessed Miguel Pro, executed by firing squad for his faith in 1927.

The ancient Catholic land of Spain is the next to fall into the grips of war and persecution, as a revolutionary government, supported and influenced by Soviet Russia, seizes control of the government in 1936. Immediately, the Church falls under persecution. Nearly 7,000 priests and religious, including thirteen bishops, are martyred, along with countless Catholic laity. Loyal Catholic soldiers rise up to battle the Communists, and after several years of bloody struggle, peace is finally restored and the persecution ended.

But there is not a moment's pause. Angry at harsh reparations that destroy the economy and longing for the restoral of national pride, Germany entrusts its future to the National Socialist Party and Adolf Hitler. Hitler plans to restore the economy and national pride through the slaughter and annihilation of others and executes his mad plan by plunging into peaceful Poland and blitzing his way through France. But world conquest is only one of Hitler's goals. Hitler hopes to eradicate all the Jews of Europe, but the Church blocks his way. Pope Pius XII leads the charge in speaking out against anti-Semitism and defiantly aiding, hiding, and saving hundreds of thousands of Jews. Thus, the extermination of the Church becomes another of Hitler's goals, and thousands of priests are sent to the concentration camp at Dachau, while three million Catholics die in Auschwitz alone, among them St. Maximilian Kolbe and St. Teresa Benedicta of the Cross (Edith Stein). By the time World War II ends in Europe, fifty million lives have been sacrificed. In the Pacific, the war ends with the dropping of atomic bombs, one of which explodes directly above Nagasaki's St. Mary Catholic Cathedral.

Since the dawn of human history, man has never known such wide-spread sorrows. Not since the persecutions of the Roman Empire has the Church been so relentlessly terrorized. The forces of darkness bask in their triumphs, but hope remains, as Pope Pius XII urges the faithful to turn to the Blessed Mother, whose bodily Assumption into heaven is declared a dogma of the Faith.

B. Learn the Story

View Track 18, *A World at War,* of the *Epic: A Journey through Church History* 20-Week Study DVD (or listen to the audio CD). Follow the presentation by referring to your *Epic* Church History Timeline Chart.

NOTES

C. Take a Deeper Look

Answering these questions will help you learn the story of the Church. If other questions come to mind write them down to discuss in the group.

1. World War I was a barbaric conflict that originated almost by happenstance. Why did Europe tear itself apart in this bloody war?

2. What was the message delivered by the Blessed Virgin Mary at Fatima? What signs did God give to show that the apparitions of Fatima were both authentic and important?

3. What have you learned about the persecution of the Church in Mexico? Who was Blessed Miguel Pro?

4. During World War II, Hitler persecuted not only Jews but also millions of Catholics. What do you think motivated this persecution? Who were some of the Catholic martyrs of the Nazi prison camps?

5. Modern critics accuse the Catholic Church of cooperating with the Nazis and even condoning Nazi anti-Semitism. Pope Pius XII has been labeled "Hitler's pope." How can you refute these absurd myths?

6. In many ways, the terrible wars of this time period are a direct result of the flourishing of modernism. What connections can you draw between the philosophy of modernism and the advent of the "modern war"?

7. History shows that invisible powers often hold great influence over human battles. Throughout this study, we have seen several examples of armies receiving divine aid at a critical moment: Constantine at the Milvian Bridge, the First Crusaders at Antioch and Jerusalem, St. Joan at Orléans, Don Juan at Lepanto, Sobieski at the Siege of Vienna. While this age was witness to the grace of God present in the millions of martyrs and saintly popes, there are hints of a dark power at play as well. What were some of the signs that suggest evil was aiding Lenin, Stalin, Hitler, and the other revolutionaries?

The Miracle of the Sun – 1917

A spectacle unique and incredible if one had not been a witness of it . . . One can see the immense crowd turn toward the sun, which reveals itself free of the clouds in full noon. The great star of day makes one think of a silver plaque, and it is possible to look straight at it without the least discomfort. It does not burn, it does not blind. It might be like an eclipse. But now bursts forth a colossal clamor, and we hear the nearest spectators crying, "Miracle, miracle! Marvel, marvel!" Before the astonished eyes of the people, whose attitude carries us back to biblical times and who, full of terror, heads uncovered, gaze into the blue of the sky, the sun has trembled, and the sun has made some brusque movements, unprecedented and outside of all cosmic laws – the sun has "danced."

– As quoted in Warren H. Carroll, *1917: Red Banners, White Mantle*

D. Application

This question asks you to think about how the lessons of history apply to today—either to the Church, to society, or to you. After meditating on this question, spend time with God in prayer.

The twentieth century was witness to the worst atrocities and bloodshed in human history, including the severe and constant persecution of the Church and her faithful. Not since the early days of the Church has she been called upon to offer such a witness. Although, for the most part, persecution through bloodshed has stopped, it can easily be restarted in a secular culture of death hostile to the culture of life. Indeed, at the October 2007 beatification of 498 martyrs of the Spanish Civil War, Pope Benedict said, "The supreme witness of giving blood is not an exception reserved only to some individuals, but a realistic possibility for all Christian people." What are some things you can do to ensure you are ready in case you should face violent persecution in the future?

Dear Lord …

E. Wrap-up

Conclude your study of the A World at War period and remember the main events by doing the following:

1. What is the color of this time period? How can you remember it?

2. What is the main theme of this period?

3. Write a one- or two-sentence summary of the A World at War period in order to recall the main events of Church history during this time.

F. Further Reading

For those who want to pursue outside readings, here is a list of good books that cover this time period whose authors approach the subject of Church history and Western civilization from a Catholic worldview. This list is not exhaustive but is provided as a starting point. Happy reading!

Blet, Pierre, S.J. *Pius XII and the Second World War according to the Archives of the Vatican.* New York: Paulist Press, 1999. *Blet provides a summation of the twelve volumes of Vatican archival wartime information on Pius XII and his efforts to help the Allies and the Jews.*

Carroll, Warren H. *1917: Red Banners, White Mantle.* Front Royal, VA: Christendom Press, 1981. *A compact history of the rise of Communism in Russia. This book explores the influences of Rasputin, Stalin, and Lenin while setting everything in the context of World War I.*

Ciszek, Walter J., S.J. with Flaherty, Daniel K., S.J. *With God in Russia.* San Francisco: Ignatius Press, 1997. *A riveting account of the activities of a Jesuit missionary in Russia during the twentieth century. Father Ciszek was arrested by the Communist authorities, accused of spying for the Vatican, and sentenced to prison in Siberia – where he stayed for twenty-three years.*

_____. *He Leadeth Me.* San Francisco: Ignatius Press, 1995. *Father Ciszek's spiritual journal of his time in Russia where he reflects on the spiritual lessons of his imprisonment.*

Dalin, Rabbi David, G. *The Myth of Hitler's Pope: How Pope Pius XII Rescued Jews from the Nazis.* Washington, DC: Regnery Publishing, Inc., 2005. *A thorough defense of Pope Pius XII against modern critics who claim he was in league with the Nazis.*

Keegan, John. *The First World War.* New York: Alfred A. Knopf, 1999. *An excellent overview of the Great War by the top-notch military historian of our time.*

_____. *The Second World War.* New York: Penguin Books, 2005. *Another excellent work by Keegan. Explores both fronts of the war with penetrating analysis and riveting narrative.*

McFadden, Charles J. *The Philosophy of Communism.* New York: Benziger Brothers, Inc., 1963. *Recommended by Archbishop Fulton Sheen and Catholic historian Dr. Diane Moczar as the best treatment of Communism in any language. The first half of the book is designed to persuade the reader with Communist arguments. The second half of the book reveals the inherent errors of those arguments.*

Royal, Robert. *The Catholic Martyrs of the 20th Century: A Comprehensive World History.* New York: Crossroads Publishing Company, 2000. *A moving work providing the historical background to the fierce and widespread persecution of the Church in the twentieth century complete with the stories of the holy martyrs of this time period.*

Rychlak, Ronald J. *Hitler, the War and the Pope.* Huntington, IN: Our Sunday Visitor, 2000. *One of the first works defending Pius XII and dismantling the modern myths concerning his wartime efforts regarding the Jews.*

EPIC

The New Springtime

A. Establish the Context

With the passing of the years, the Council documents have lost nothing of their value or brilliance. They need to be read correctly, to be widely known and taken to heart ... [The Second Vatican Council was] the great grace bestowed on the Church in the twentieth century: there we find a sure compass by which to take our bearings in the century now beginning."

– John Paul II, *Novo Millennio Ineunte*, 57

Number of bishops at Vatican II
2,300

"Christ, the one Mediator, established and continually sustains here on earth His holy Church, the community of faith, hope and charity, as an entity with visible deliniation through which He communicates truth and grace to all."
– *Lumen Gentium*, 8

Facing an unprecedented identity crisis after two horrific world wars, Europe is in need of the saving message of Jesus Christ. Recognizing the desperate need to give Europe and the world the gift of hope, Pope Bl. John XXIII calls the Second Vatican Council. The council is meant to be a positive experience for the Church, an opportunity to sharpen the language and techniques used to spread the Gospel. Unlike previous councils, this gathering is not intended to solve any major doctrinal issues or pass pressing disciplinary canons; rather, its focus is on presenting the truth and demonstrating the validity of teachings rather than demanding unthinking obedience or issuing condemnations. Bl. John XXIII recognizes that modern man is different and the "whys" of the Church's teaching must be presented in ways that speak to him rather than a rote recitation of the "whats."

Unfortunately, "Good Pope John" does not live to see his dream completed, dying after the first session of the council. His successor, Paul VI, takes up the conciliar mantle and finishes the work. The Council produces sixteen major documents on wide-ranging subjects; four of which are major constitutions discussing the liturgy, the Church, divine revelation, and the role of the Church in the modern world. The Church is well positioned to bring the Light of Christ to a damaged Europe and a changing world. However, something happens after the council. The implementation is less than ideal, and certain elements within the Church misuse the Council and its documents to forge their own path in contradiction to the authentic teaching. While history shows it takes a generation for the full and authentic implementation of a council's teachings, the forty-year period after the Second Vatican Council is a stressful one that threatens to destroy the unity of the Church, creating groups who call themselves Catholic but reject the true teachings of the council. Some groups use the teachings of the council to further their own political and social agendas, while others deride the Council and blame it for the ills infecting the Church. The hope of the Council gives way to a crisis, but hope will return.

The men called to the Petrine Office have always upheld the duty of instructing the faithful and, as a result, have written numerous works on various subjects. This period is witness to several great papal writings addressing the pressing needs of the modern world through the ancient teaching of the Gospel. Bl. John XXIII issued a masterful social encyclical entitled *Mater et Magistra* (1961) wherein he builds upon the Church's social teachings artfully enumerated by Pope Leo XIII in his groundbreaking encyclical letter *Rerum Novarum* (1891). Bl. John XXIII reminds the world of the correct placement of the state in the life of the individual and calls wealthy developed nations to exercise Christian charity and fraternity to poorer nations in need. Concerned with the growing confrontation between the nuclear powers engaged in a "Cold War," Bl. John XXIII wrote *Pacem in Terris* (1963) to call for an end to the "arms race." Pope Paul VI was faced with a very important cultural situation during the late 1960s, which questioned and challenged many previously held societal norms. Advances in the medical field provided new technologies that some argued were of great benefit to humanity, especially to married couples. The invention of the anovulent birth control pill challenged the apostolic teaching of the Church on human sexuality and the inadmissibility of contraception. Responding to these questions, Paul VI expanded the papal commission appointed by Bl. John XXIII to study the matter. The Commission delivered their report and Paul VI deliberated and prayed. His response was a beautiful document reiterating the constant teaching of the Church on the truth and meaning of marriage and human sexuality. This document, *Humanae Vitae*, however, proved a lightening rod for criticism and rebellion as many within the Church called for a rejection of the teaching. The subsequent revolution had a severe negative impact; only recently has a catechesis been developed to adequately explain the truth and beauty of this misunderstood teaching.

Although the initial period after the Second Vatican Council was witness to some confusion and difficulty in implementation, one of the main fruits of the Council was a rise in the development and acceptance of the "ecclesial movements." These groups of dedicated and devoted Catholic laity stressed the living out of the "universal call to holiness," one of the main themes of the Council. These movements have shaped lay participation in the life of the Church and are an essential ingredient of the "New Springtime."

B. Learn the Story

View Track 19, *The New Springtime,* of the *Epic: A Journey through Church History* 20-Week Study DVD (or listen to the audio CD). Follow the presentation by referring to your *Epic* Church History Timeline Chart.

NOTES

C. Take a Deeper Look

Answering these questions will help you learn the story of the Church. If other questions come to mind, write them down to discuss in the group.

1.   Why did Pope Bl. John XXIII call the Second Vatican Council? What was the council's main task?

2.   List the four major constitutions of the Second Vatican Council and provide the main points of each.

3. It usually takes a generation for the decrees of a council to be implemented authentically. Is this statement true in reference to the Second Vatican Council?

4. Two major social justice encyclicals were written during this time period, list them and provide the main points of each.

5. Pope Paul VI promulgated *Humanae Vitae* in 1968. It is one of the most misunderstood and maligned papal writings in Church history. Why? What are its main points?

6. What are the "ecclesial movements"? List the names of a few of these groups. What are your impression of these groups?

The Beauty of Married Love

This love is above all fully human, a compound of sense and spirit. It is not, then, merely a question of natural instinct or emotional drive. It is also, and above all, an act of the free will, whose trust is such that it is meant not only to survive the joys and sorrows of daily life, but also to grow, so that husband and wife become in a way one heart and one soul, and together attain their human fulfillment. It is a love, which is total—that very special form of personal friendship in which husband and wife generously share everything ... and not thinking solely of their own convenience. Married love is also faithful and exclusive of all other, and this until death. Though this fidelity of husband and wife sometimes presents difficulties, no one has the right to assert that it is impossible; it is, on the contrary, always honorable and meritorious. Finally, this love is fecund. It is not confined wholly to the loving interchange of husband and wife; it also contrives to go beyond this to bring new life into being.

– Paul VI, *Humanae Vitae*, 9

D. Application

This question asks you to think about how the lessons of history apply to today—either to the Church, society or to you. After meditating on this question, spend time with God in prayer.

The Second Vatican Council was a watershed moment in the lives of Catholics in the twentieth century. This gathering of bishops, led by the pope and guided by the Holy Spirit was filled with a sense of hope and renewal leading to the "New Springtime." In many places around the world the council teachings were implemented successfully, in others (particularly Europe and the United States), a more difficult implementation resulted. What are your memories of the council? What has been your experience with its implementation? What can you do to aid the Church in successfully implementing the beautiful and inspired teachings of the council?

Dear Lord ...

E. Wrap-up

Conclude your study of the New Springtime period and remember the main events by doing the following:

1. What is the color of this time period? How can you remember it?

2. What is the main theme of this period?

3. Write a one or two sentence summary of the New Springtime period in order to recall the main events of Church history during this time.

F. Further Reading

For those who want to pursue outside readings, here is a list of good books that cover this time period whose authors approach the subject of Church history and Western civilization from a Catholic worldview. This list is not exhaustive but is provided as a starting point. Happy reading!

Allen, John L. Jr. *Opus Dei: An Objective Look Behind the Myths and Reality of the Most Controversial Force in the Catholic Church.* New York: Doubleday, 2005. *A penetrating look into the ecclesial movement, Opus Dei. Allen provides a brief overview of the organization and its founder as well as a look inside the membership and how they live their vocation. He raises and answers some of the major issues and criticisms leveled against the group and finishes with an evaluation of the future of Opus Dei.*

Flannery, Austin, O.P., ed. *Vatican Council II: The Conciliar and Post-Conciliar Documents.* Northport, NY: Costello Publishing Company, 1992. *The translated documents of the Council; a must read for Catholics today.*

Hahn, Scott. *Ordinary Work, Extraordinary Grace : My Spiritual Journey in Opus Dei.* New York: Doubleday, 2006. *Hahn provides an overview of Opus Dei and the teachings of St. Josemaría Escrivá in the context of living these teachings as a member of Opus Dei.*

Kelly, George Msgr. *The Battle for the American Church.* New York: Doubleday, 1979. *A frank assessment of the crisis in the Church and the failed implementation of the Council in the United States. Delves deeply into the situation of the Church in the United States, pre- and post-council. A fascinating and enlightening book.*

_____. *The Battle for the American Church (Revisited).* San Francisco: Ignatius Press, 1995. *Nearly twenty years after the book's initial publication, Kelly revisits his thesis and updates his assessment of the Church in the United States.*

Schreck, Alan. *Vatican II: The Crisis and the Promise.* Cincinnati: Servant Books/St. Anthony Messenger Press, 2005. *A review of the implementation of the council and an analysis of the future. Schreck also provides highlights of the major constitutions and many of the other documents of the council.*

Smith, Janet. *Humanae Vitae: A Generation Later.* Washington, D.C.: Catholic University Press, 1991. *Smith provides a scholarly treatment of the issue of contraception, the papal commission established to review the Church's teaching in light of modern advances, and the dissent from the teaching. This work also provides a thorough analysis from philosophical and theological reasoning of why the Church teaches that contraception is intrinsically evil. This work also includes an author's translation of the encyclical from the Latin and a commentary.*

The Threshold of Hope & Conclusion

A. Establish the Context

"It is very important to cross the threshold of hope, not to stop before it, but to let oneself be led. I believe that the great Polish poet Cyprian Norwid had this in mind when he expressed the ultimate meaning of the Christian life in these words: 'Not with the Cross of the Savoir behind you, but with your own cross behind the Savior.' There is every reason for the truth of the Cross to be called the Good News."

– John Paul II, *Crossing the Threshold of Hope*

The year 1978 was a momentous one in Church history. It was the "year of the three popes," and it was witness to the rise of one of the truly great pontiffs, John Paul II. After the untimely death and short reign (only thirty-three days) of John Paul I, the cardinals gathered in conclave to elect a successor to St. Peter. The world and the Church were in a precarious place. Communism had firmly grasped the territories of Eastern Europe and was engaged in a military, economic, political, and cultural Cold War with Western civilization. The promise of the Second Vatican Council had given way to a crisis of implementation in Western Europe and the United States. The next pope would be challenged in ways unimaginable by his predecessors. On October 16, 1978, the first Polish pope (and first non-Italian Pope in 455 years) in Church history addressed the eager crowd gathered in St. Peter's Square. Karol Cardinal Wojtyla, now John Paul II, raised his hands in blessing and said, "Be not afraid." This simple sentence uttered in the Scriptures by angelic visitors became the watchwords of a twenty-seven-year pontificate that shaped world and Church history.

The writings of Pope John Paul II
14 encyclicals
11 apostolic constitutions
15 apostolic exhortations
45 apostolic letters
5 books

Number of saints canonized by John Paul II
482

John Paul II received his "training" for the papacy in his Polish homeland. His firsthand experience with the Nazi and communist regimes helped him draw closer to the Gospel and develop the means to preach the message of Christ effectively to those who lacked hope and trust in their fellow man. As a member of the episcopacy, he led his flock in peaceful protests against the communist regime. He also led the Polish faithful to an understanding and acceptance of the documents of the Second Vatican Council. A prolific writer throughout his life, he wrote books on the authentic implementation of the council (*Sources of Renewal*) and married love (*Love and Responsibility*), subjects that would form the foundation of his pontifical teaching.

His papacy was unique in its expression. John Paul II changed the way the modern world views the pope. His multiple apostolic visits increased the visibility of the papacy and provided an international platform for the preaching of the Gospel. His papacy embodied the teachings of the Second Vatican Council by embracing authentic ecumenism, renewing devotion to the Blessed Virgin Mary and exercising the papal magisterium. He promulgated fourteen encyclicals, wrote forty-five apostolic letters and published five books. His institution of the World Youth Days was a brilliant strategy to bring the Gospel to the youth and foster in them a love of Christ and His Church. Affirming the "universal call to holiness," John Paul II greatly expanded the company of men and women honored at the altar as saints and blesseds. He led the Church through the Great Jubilee and the celebration of the dawning of a new millennium of the Christian Faith. Before he left this world to journey on in the next, he gave the Church a necessary and authentic blueprint to boldly proclaim the Gospel in the third millennium by highlighting the words of Christ to "put out into the deep!" Very few men, called by God to the Chair of Peter, have not only lived that call authentically but by their words and work, sanctified the office as well. Truly, John Paul II can be considered among the great popes in the history of the Church.

The beloved John Paul II, after a long and debilitating illness, passed into eternal glory on April 2, 2005. His trusted advisor and friend, Joseph Cardinal Ratzinger, was elected his successor, taking the name Benedict XVI. After 2,000 years, the Church continues to endure despite the human weaknesses of her members. Animated by the Holy Spirit, the Church continues to fulfill the mission entrusted to her by her Lord and Master. Holy men and women continue to respond to the Gospel call to live lives at odds with a culture that no longer binds itself to the Faith. Although many dark clouds hover over the future, the Church carries the banner of her Lord high, trusting in His grace, the protection of His Mother and the intercession of His holy ones. The tiny band of brothers that began the epic journey of the Church 2,000 years ago has grown to a multitude of followers who continue to march onward, crossing the threshold of hope, awaiting the return of the King.

B. Learn the Story

View Track 20, *The Threshold of Hope & Conclusion*, of the *Epic: A Journey through Church History* 20-Week Study DVD (or listen to the audio CD). Follow the presentation by referring to your *Epic* Church History Timeline Chart.

NOTES

C. Take a Deeper Look

Answering these questions will help you learn the story of the Church. If other questions come to mind write them down to discuss in the group.

1. What were the first public words uttered by John Paul II upon his election in 1978? Why do you think he chose those words?

2. List some of John Paul II's encyclicals. What are their topics? Which one is your favorite?

3. What were the main themes of John Paul II's pontificate? Why did he choose those themes?

4. John Paul II greatly expanded the number of holy men and women honored by the Church as saints. Name some of these saints. Do you have a special devotion to one of these saints? If so, share the story of this saint and your devotion to him or her with the group.

5. Some people have already begun to refer to Pope John Paul as "John Paul the Great." Who are the other "Great" popes in Church history? Should John Paul II be called "the Great"? Why or why not?

6. What are some of the major issues facing the Church in the third millennium of the Faith?

7. You are now at the conclusion of this study; answer the following questions about your twenty-week *Epic* journey:

   a. What time period(s) most interested you? Why?

   b. What is the most important thing you have learned studying Church history?

   c. What time period(s) would you like to delve into deeper?

   d. Using your *Epic* chart, trace the twenty-one ecumenical councils. What can they tell you about the story of the Church?

   e. What role can you play in the continuing story of the Church?

> ***People of Light***
>
> Life is like a voyage on the sea of history, often dark and stormy, a voyage in which we watch for the stars that indicate the route. The true stars of our life are the people who have lived good lives. They are lights of hope. Certainly, Jesus Christ is the true light, the sun that has risen above all the shadows of history. But to reach Him we also need lights close by—people who shine with his light and so guide us along our way.
>
> – Benedict XVI, *Spe Salvi*, 49

D. Application

This question asks you to think about how the lessons of history apply to today—either to the Church, to society, or to you. After meditating on this question, spend time with God in prayer.

Pope John Paul II shaped the lives of many Catholics. Many young priests or those currently studying for the priesthood trace the origin of their vocation to John Paul II's witness and outreach to youth. Numerous families have chosen to name their sons John Paul in honor of the late Holy Father. His long reign and charismatic personality are some of the reasons for the tremendous devotion and love for the Polish Pope. What are your memories of Pope John Paul II? What actions or writings influenced your life the most? How has John Paul II's pontificate enriched your life as a Catholic?

Dear Lord …

E. Wrap-up

Conclude your study of the Threshold of Hope time period and remember the main events by doing the following:

1. What is the color of this time period? How can you remember it?

2. What is the main theme of this period?

3. Write a one- or two-sentence summary of the Threshold of Hope period in order to recall the main events of Church history during this time.

F.   Further Reading

For those who want to pursue outside readings, here is a list of good books that cover this time period whose authors approach the subject of Church history and Western civilization from a Catholic worldview. This list is not exhaustive but is provided as a starting point. Happy reading!

John Paul II. *The Theology of the Body: Human Love in the Divine Plan.* Boston: Pauline Books and Media, 1997. *The translated Wednesday afternoon catecheses Pope John Paul II delivered from 1981–1984 outlining his thoughts on the human person, marriage, and married love.*

Ratzinger, Joseph Cardinal. *Europe: Today and Tomorrow – Addressing the Fundamental Issues.* San Francisco: Ignatius Press, 2007. *Before his election to the papacy, Cardinal Ratzinger wrote and spoke on the most pressing questions facing Europe in the new millennium. He reflects on the history of Europe, her roots and her future.*

_____. *The Ratzinger Report: An Exclusive Interview on the State of the Church.* With Vittorio Messori. San Francisco: Ignatius Press, 1985. *While Prefect for the Congregation for the Doctrine of the Faith, Cardinal Ratzinger spoke with an Italian journalist on the state of the Church. A fascinating and enlightening interview and worth the read.*

_____. *Salt of the Earth: The Church at the End of the Millennium – An Interview with Peter Seewald.* San Francisco: Ignatius Press, 1997. *A little more than ten years after the* Ratzinger Report, *this work addresses the pressing issues in the Church and Cardinal Ratzinger's thoughts and analysis.*

_____. *God and the World: Believing and Living in Our Time – A Conversation with Peter Seewald.* San Francisco: Ignatius Press, 2002. *Another book length interview with German journalist Peter Seewald. This work focuses on who is God, what is Faith, and what it means to believe while residing in the modern world.*

Weigel, George. *Witness to Hope: The Biography of Pope John Paul II.* New York: HarperCollins, 1999. *The definitive biography of John Paul II, tracing his life from childhood through his pontificate. Filled with fascinating and insightful stories on the life of this amazing man. The events of the pontificate are placed in context with the larger political and economic events.*

_____. *The Cube and the Cathedral: Europe, America and Politics without God.* New York: Basic Books, 2005. *A frank assessment of the situation of Europe in light of her relationship with the United States and her disassociation from her Catholic roots.*

Wojtyla, Karol. *Love and Responsibility.* San Francisco: Ignatius Press, 1993. *A discussion of the human vocation to love and the responsibility it entails with a focus on married love. An excellent work that sheds light on the meaning of a much misunderstood action.*

Introduction & Mustard Seed

A. Review the Context

Discussion Leaders: Make sure everyone has an *Epic* Church History Timeline chart to use when discussing questions about the time period. Briefly go over the other sections of the chart—especially the Events & Influences section—so that you can situate the story of the Church in the larger story of the world.

B. Learn the Story

Discussion Leaders: Unless there are comments or questions about Steve Weidenkopf's presentation, dive into answering the discussion questions in Section C.

C. Take a Deeper Look

Introduction: What is history?

1. *Why do we like stories? Why are they important to us?*

   Answers will vary, but ultimately, we like stories because God is a storyteller—or, more precisely, God is an *author*. The Scriptures and the lives of human beings throughout the centuries give witness to God's storyteller nature. We also like stories because they foster a sense of relationship and sharing. We are made in God's image and likeness, and since God is relational, we too greatly desire to be in relationship with others. When we read a good book or see a good movie, we desire to share that experience with others. We do this because we are relational and we desire to live life as a shared adventure (this sense of life as a shared adventure finds its expression in our vocation, particularly in the sacrament of marriage).

   Stories are important to us because life makes sense when understood as a story. Kurt Bruner, author of *The Divine Drama*, summed this up nicely: "The meaning of life can be found in story, and the meaning of story can be found in life." Stories give shape to our lives and they help us remember our history.

2. *Jesus spoke to His disciples in parables. List some of these parables. Which is your favorite? Why?*

   Parables are the stories Jesus told in which He describes the kingdom of God and invites us to the heavenly feast (See *Catechism* No. 546)

   Here is a partial listing of the parables of Christ:

   The Mustard Seed (*Matthew 13:31-32; Mark 4:31-32; Luke 13:18-19*)
   The Sower (*Matthew 13:3-8; Mark 4:3-8; Luke 8:5-8*)
   The Pearl of Price (*Matthew 13:45*)
   The Unmerciful Servant (*Matthew 18:21-35*)
   The Laborers in the Vineyard (*Matthew 20:1-16*)
   The Ten Virgins (*Matthew 25:1-13*)
   The Unjust Steward (*Luke 16:1-9*)
   The Prodigal Son (*Luke 15:11-32*)

3. *Is history important? Why should we study it?*

History is important because it is our story and remembering this story is vital to the life of a nation. Pope John Paul II recognized the importance of history when he wrote: "History is an essential element of culture" (*Memory & Identity*, 74). A nation that loses its story is a nation whose culture is weakened and that weakness will pervade all aspects of society. The Church's story is rich and must be learned and remembered in order to strength the identification of her members with her in order to continue the work of evangelization.

4. *Hilaire Belloc spoke of a "Catholic conscience of history." What is this? Do you have it? If so, how did you acquire it? If not, why not?*

Hilaire Belloc (1870–1953), in his famous work *Europe and the Faith* (1920), writes of a "Catholic conscience of history." What he means is "an intimate knowledge through identity." A Catholic is one whose very identification with the Church produces an understanding of the history of the Church and Western civilization. In the words of Belloc, "The Catholic brings to history self-knowledge." Belloc's thought strikes at the core of Catholic life. A Catholic is a member of the greatest organization in the history of the world, an entity that has significantly shaped human events for the past 2,000 years. In essence, Catholics are inheritors of this great story, even if they don't know it. However, it is vital to the life of Catholics and to the life of the Church that the story be learned and remembered. Unfortunately, the story has been obscured over the last century or so by those who take issue with the Church and her teaching. This is why Belloc spent the latter years of his life writing history books from a Catholic world-view in order to combat the prevalent Protestant worldview found in history books.

5. *As Catholics how do we understand history?*

Ancient Greek and Roman historians presented history as a series of repetitive cycles. St. Augustine (A.D. 354–430) saw history as linear, punctuated by climaxes and overseen by God, who is involved in human events. For the Catholic, history has a definitive beginning (creation) and end (the return of Christ). The central event in human history is the Incarnation—all history radiates outward from this point. Christ is the key to human history and it cannot be properly understood without an emphasis on Him (see *Catechism* No. 450).

Mustard Seed

1. *What event marks the beginning of the Church? What happened?*

Pentecost. The Holy Spirit descended on the apostles and the Blessed Mother ten days after the Ascension. This event marked the beginning of the Church and its great adventure to spread the Gospel throughout history. St. Peter begins this journey with a powerful proclamation of Christ and His mission. This witness is followed by the conversion of 3,000—the first converts in Church history. Read **Acts 2** for the full story.

2. *What was the major topic of discussion at the Council of Jerusalem? How was the issue resolved?*

The issue at hand was whether Gentile converts to the Faith needed to be circumcised and follow the Jewish dietary laws. Division among the apostles centered on St. James the Less, bishop of Jerusalem, who favored Gentile acceptance of the Law, and St. Paul, who did not. After discussion, it was St. Peter who provided the opinion that prevailed—the Gentiles did not have to be circumcised and only had to refrain from eating meat offered to false gods, and the flesh of strangled animals. Read **Acts 15:1–20**.

3. *Why did persecution of Christians erupt in A.D. 64? Was the persecution widespread? What was its effect?*

The mad Roman emperor Nero ordered the burning of a particular section of the city of Rome. The fire quickly went out of control and the city suffered significant damage. After public outcry, and in order to deflect criticism, Nero blamed the Christians for the fire. The persecution of Christians was limited to Rome, but it did lead to the empire-wide outlawing of the Christian Faith (a law which would not be repealed for almost 250 years—in A.D. 313). Sts. Peter and Paul were martyred during this persecution, a persecution which produced sympathy for Christians among the Roman people.

4. *What are the key points raised in Pope St. Clement's letter to the Corinthians?*

There are three main points raised in the very important Epistle of Pope St. Clement.

1. Church officials do not derive their authority from the people but from God.

2. Apostolic succession.

3. The universal primacy of the bishop of Rome.

Before the year A.D. 100, the Church's teachings on bishops and especially the bishop of Rome is explicitly mentioned and taught by the Holy Father. This letter was highly revered by the early Christians and was considered second only to the Scriptures in authority.

D. Application

Discussion Leaders: If time permits, ask the group members to share their personal responses to the application question.

The apostles went beyond the known world to begin the spread of the Gospel. How were they able to accomplish such a feat? What was your journey of faith? Who first brought the Gospel to your attention? Who have you spread the Gospel to?

Close with the prayer found in the Leader's Guide.

E. Wrap-up

1. *What is the color of this time period? How can you remember it?*

Remember the Mustard Seed time period by its color, mustard yellow: a reminder of the parable of the Kingdom of God as a mustard seed (Mark 4:30-32).

2. *What is the main theme of this period?*

The main theme of the Mustard Seed period is the beginning of the Church and the start of the Church's mission to spread the Gospel.

3. *Write a one- or two-sentence summary of the Mustard Seed period in order to recall the main events of Church history during this time.*

Answers will vary but they should contain most of the main events listed on the *Epic* Church History Timeline chart.

Persecution – Part I

A. Review the Context

Discussion Leaders: Make sure everyone has their *Epic* Church History Timeline chart to use when discussing questions about the time period. Briefly go over the other sections of the chart—especially the Events & Influences section—so that you can situate the story of the Church in the larger story of the world.

B. Learn the Story

Discussion Leaders: Unless there are comments or questions about Steve Weidenkopf's presentation, dive into answering the discussion questions in Section C.

C. Take a Deeper Look

1. *What was the Church in the Roman Empire? Give some of its characteristics.*

    The Church was a distinct and unique organization within the Empire. She had grown up *within* the Empire but was not *of* the Empire. The Church was highly disciplined, united, hierarchically organized, growing, institution that held to exact and unwavering doctrines. Central among these doctrines was the Incarnation of God in a historical person, Jesus Christ. The Church also held firmly to the belief of the Real Presence of Jesus (His body, blood, soul, and divinity) under the appearance of bread and wine in the Eucharist.

2. *What were some of the pagan myths used to slander the early Church? Are these myths still used today?*

    Pagan critics and propagandists accused Christians for attracting the poor and ignorant, believing in unreasonable superstitions, committing depraved acts of sexual immorality, and engaging in treasonous behavior.

    Not surprisingly, there are many modern myths used against the Church, and many of them follow the same pattern. Following the example of the early apologists, the best way to handle these myths is to arm one's self with the facts and be prepared to give a reasonable, not emotional, response. Since many of these allegations are based on a corrupt or incomplete understanding of history, learning the story of the Church can be a key weapon in defending her against false charges.

3. *Why did the Roman Empire persecute the Church? Do you think such persecution could happen in our modern world?*

    There are many reasons for the persecution of Christians in the Empire. Chief among them is imperial politics. The emperors used the persecutions to deflect criticism of their rule, to satiate the mob and to enforce imperial unity. The Christians threatened the Roman establishment by their refusal to worship the state deities. Although temporal reasons can help explain why the emperors used persecution, we cannot overlook the importance of the spiritual sphere. Roman society, in many ways, was guided by an anti-life demonically influenced worldview. A spiritual battle, along with the temporal, was fought during this time period between the forces of good and evil. The blood of the martyrs ensured victory for those who followed the Light.

Persecution of Christians has been a constant theme since the beginning of the Church. Persecution continues in our modern world, many times taking the form of violent persecution (as in the Sudan, for example) but also as a "white" persecution. For example, our modern society struggles with how the Faith should be expressed in the public square (or whether it should be expressed at all). Christian teaching is openly ridiculed in the media and many suffer verbal insults for the Faith. We can take solace in the fact that thousands of years ago Christians underwent the same treatment yet remained strong in their faith. Their witness preserved the Church and eventually allowed her to spread the Gospel throughout the world.

4. *St. Ignatius, Bishop of Antioch, wrote seven letters on his way to be martyred in Rome. What are some of the important points made in these early Christian writings?*

St. Ignatius wrote letters to the Ephesians, Magnesians, Trallians, Romans, Smyrnaeans, Philadelphians, and St. Polycarp. St. Ignatius outlines many important points about the Faith of the early Church, including the belief in the Real Presence of Christ in the Eucharist, the Divinity of Christ, the hierarchical structure (i.e. bishops, priests, deacons, laity) of the Church, the importance of the Church of Rome, and the understanding of Mary as Mother of God. He also gave the Church her name by being the first to refer to her as the "Catholic Church."

5. *During this time, heresies arose to attack the Church from within. What were some of the early heresies of the Church, and what were some of their mistaken beliefs?*

GNOSTICISM. This heresy was based on a dualist system that believed there was a "god of light" and a "god of darkness." It condemned the material world as the creation of the "evil god" and claimed the human soul was "trapped" in a physical body, making suicide the highest form of worship. It denied the Incarnation and held that the sacraments—including marriage and marital relations—were evil because they were material in nature. It claimed that there was a secret knowledge held by only an elect few, the Perfect, that could lead to purification. This heresy would mutate into various strains throughout Church history including the Manicheans (fourth century) and the Albigensians (thirteenth century).

MARCIONISM. A semi-Gnostic heresy started by Marcion in A.D. 144. It believed there was a dichotomy between the Old and New Testaments, and, similar to Gnosticism, that the Old Testament God was evil and the New Testament God was good. It also denied that Jesus had a human nature.

MONTANISM. Started in the late second century by Montanus who claimed to receive direct revelation from the Holy Spirit. He took a position of extreme asceticism and moral rigorism. This heresy called for its followers to reject all earthly pleasures and repudiate all civil obligations. It also believed that sins committed after the reception of baptism could not be forgiven.

D. Application

Discussion Leaders: If time permits, ask the group members to share their personal responses to the application question.

St. Justin Martyr wrote a defense of the Faith to the Roman emperor Antoninus Pius. Many others rose up to fight the myths and lies being spread about the Christians by Roman society. What are some of the modern day myths and lies told about the Church and her teachings? Share an experience where you defended the Faith. What are some effective ways to counter the misrepresentation and misinformation of the Faith in our modern world?

Close with the prayer found in the Leader's Guide.

Persecution – Part II

A. Review the Context

Discussion Leaders: Make sure everyone has their *Epic* Church History Timeline chart to use when discussing questions about the time period. Briefly go over the other sections of the chart—especially the Events & Influences section—so that you can situate the story of the Church in the larger story of the world.

B. Learn the Story

Discussion Leaders: Unless there are comments or questions about Steve Weidenkopf's presentation, dive into answering the discussion questions in Section C.

C. Take a Deeper Look

1. *The early Church Fathers defended the Faith by explaining it to the Romans and fighting the errors of heretics. Who were some of these first apologists? Why are they important?*

   The early Church Fathers are important because they recorded the beliefs of the early Christians. Their powerful testimony shows that the fundamental dogmas of the Catholic Faith, such as belief in the Real Presence of Christ in the Eucharist, the Holy Trinity, the Divinity of Christ, Mary's role as Mother of God, the primacy of the bishop of Rome, and the existence of the hierarchy of pope, bishops, and priests, were a part of the Christian Faith since the beginning. Some of the notable Church Fathers of this period are St. Ignatius, Bishop of Antioch (d. 115), St. Justin Martyr (d. 165), St. Irenaeus (c. 185), Tertullian (d. 230), and Origen (d. 254).

2. *Tertullian was one of the great early Church Fathers who defended the faith from pagan critics. His early work is even quoted in the Catechism of the Catholic Church. Yet, despite his brilliance and devotion, he died a heretic. What lessons can we learn from Tertullian's tragic fall?*

   There are many lessons that can be learned from Tertullian's sad example. One is that pride can be a fatal stumbling block, even for those committed to defending the Faith. Tertullian's insistence that he was smarter and holier than anyone, including the pope, has been a snare for Catholics throughout history. It is important for all Christians, especially those who wish to study and intellectually defend the faith, to remember, "Fear of God is the source of all wisdom." Sometimes we might struggle with particular Church teachings and ask many questions but we should do so with an understanding that the presumption of truth rests with the Church. She has been endowed with the authority of Christ and safeguarded by the Holy Spirit to authoritatively and authentically interpret and teach on matters of faith and morals.

   Another valuable lesson is that fixation upon the immoral behavior of others can blind us to our own faults. Tertullian's outrage at the leniency afforded by the Church to those who had fallen back into sin calls to mind the indignant older brother in the parable of the Prodigal Son (Luke 15:28-30). While we must, to a degree, be cognizant of the immoral *acts* of public figures, such as the misbehavior of a politician or a member of the clergy, we must always be careful not to pass judgment on the *person* himself. If we get too caught up in condemning those whom we believe have not merited forgiveness, we may be surprised to find a great "log" in our own eye (Matthew 7:5).

3. *Overall there were twelve major persecutions under the Roman Empire. What were the names of some of the emperors that persecuted Christians during this time period? What were the dates and circumstances of these persecutions?*

The Emperor Trajan persecuted Christians from 98 to 117. At first he tolerated Christians so long as they kept their faith hidden and allowed those who made their faith public to be arrested. However, after a severe earthquake hit Antioch, he used Christians as the scapegoat, condemning them to death including the revered St. Ignatius of Antioch.

The Emperor Decius persecuted Christians from 249 to 251. He desired a unified empire and demanded that Christians conform to the old pagan gods. He issued an edict in 250 that required every man, woman, and child to make a public sacrifice to an idol, any refusal meant death.

The Emperor Valerian persecuted Christians from 257 to 259. German tribal and Persian attacks led to chaos in the empire, and in an attempt to restore unity Valerian passed an edict demanding all bishops, priests, and deacons sacrifice to the gods or suffer exile. He then issued an edict condemning all Christian clergy to death.

The Emperor Diocletian persecuted Christians from 303 to 305. At the urging of his co-emperor, Galerius, Diocletian signed an edict terminating all civil rights for Christians and calling for churches and sacred scrolls to be destroyed. Then, after fires broke out in Nicomedia, Christians were to be arrested and tortured. When Diocletian's nerves forced him to the sidelines, Galerius released his full fury and declared that all Christians must sacrifice to the gods or die.

4. *The story of the early Church is filled with the sacrifices of great martyrs. Is there a particular martyr you admire or relate to? What is his or her story, and how did you first learn about this saint?*

Answers may vary but here are a few stories of popular martyrs.

St. Victor martyred in A.D. 290
St. Victor was a Catholic soldier of the Roman army who, upon discovery of his faith, was tortured in an attempt to force him to worship pagan gods. Not only did St. Victor remain faithful to Christ, but also when thrown in jail to recover from his wounds he converted the three soldiers guarding him. Outraged, the Roman officials took him to the temple to offer incense to Jupiter, but he defiantly kicked the idol to the ground. His foot was amputated as punishment. He was crushed to death by a millstone.

St. Perpetua & Companions martyred in A.D. 203
St. Perpetua, along with St. Felicity and four other Christians, were martyred by wild animals as part of the games held in honor of Geta Caesar. A savage cow first trampled St. Perpetua, but she was in such a state of ecstasy that others had to convince her, through the bruises on her body and torn dress, that she had been attacked. After exchanging the kiss of peace among them, the Christians faced their final execution by the sword. The gladiator who attacked St. Perpetua dealt her a painful but only glancing blow. St. Perpetua then helped the inexperienced gladiator by guiding his sword to her throat with her own hands. The record of her martyrdom says, "Perhaps so great a woman, feared by the unclean spirit, could not have been slain unless she so willed it."

St. Lawrence martyred in A.D. 258
St. Lawrence was the head deacon in Rome, which made him responsible for Church funds. The prefect of the city demanded that the treasures of the Church be given to him for the good of the empire, and St. Lawrence agreed. After taking inventory for three days, St. Lawrence led the prefect to a church filled with the poor and the sick saying, "These are the treasures that adorn Christ's temple." Furious,

the prefect ordered St. Lawrence to die by being slowly roasted alive over an iron grate. After many hours, St. Lawrence called out, "Turn me over, this side is well done."

5. *Christians presented no real threat to the Roman Empire, since they were, for the most part, tax-paying, law-abiding citizens, yet they were consistently persecuted. St. Justin Martyr explained why by saying, "The world suffers nothing from Christians but hates them because they reject its pleasures." What do you think he meant?*

There are many themes contained in this one sentence. While there was certainly some amount of greed involved in the early persecutions, since an accused Christian often forfeited his land and possessions, there was also something more profound at play. The Roman world was filled with sin, especially ruthless violence and sexual deviancy. Public executions were entertainment for the masses, and abortion and infanticide were very common occurrences. Christians, by not participating in these immoral activities, were clearly judging them as unacceptable behavior. Many who enjoyed these illicit acts naturally felt guilty, ashamed, and angry with those who refused to accept or condone their ways.

This is a universal theme, as attested to by Christ's teaching that Christians must be "not of the world" (John 15:18) and "will have tribulations in the world" (John 16:23). It can be seen in every age, even today.

6. *One of the great difficulties the early Church faced was how to deal with lapsi, or lapsed Catholics who fell away from the faith during persecution. Why do you think this was such a difficult problem? Is this a problem in the Church today?*

There can be different answers to this question, but the fundamental conflict is centered on an understanding of God's divine justice and mercy. Many of those who objected to the forgiveness of the *lapsi* were moral rigorists who wanted to put a limit on God's mercy. They felt that allowing public sinners who had turned their back on Christ to return to the Church would make a mockery of God's justice. The Church, while acknowledging the debt owed to Divine Justice by assigning strict penances to the returning *lapsi*, nevertheless understood that it is not wise to limit God's unfathomable mercy.

D. Application

Discussion Leaders: If time permits, ask the group members to share their personal responses to the application question.

"The blood of martyrs is the seed of Christians," said Tertullian. Persecution was the ultimate test for the early Christians. Many martyrs, like St. Perpetua, went to their death while their close friends and families pleaded with them to turn away from their faith and save their lives. Often, the only thing asked of them was to offer one tiny pinch of incense to an idol, but they refused to compromise their faith. While the modern world, in most cases, does not openly persecute Christians, it does encourage us to make small compromises with our faith so as not to offend others. We are constantly told by those around us not to take religion "too seriously." How are you called to suffer for the Faith in today's world? What can you do to foster a faith that will never compromise?

Close with the prayer found in the Leader's Guide.

E. Wrap-up

1.   What is the color of this time period? How can you remember it?

Remember the Persecution time period by its color, dark red: a reminder of the blood of the martyrs.

2.   What is the main theme of this period?

The main theme of the Persecution period is the triumph of the Church against all odds, thriving despite the bloody persecutions of the Roman Empire and preserving the true Faith against the errors of the heretics.

3.   Write a one- or two-sentence summary of the Persecution period in order to recall the main events of Church history during this time.

Answers will vary but they should contain most of the main events listed on the *Epic* Church History Timeline chart.

Conversion & Councils – Part I

A. Review the Context

Discussion Leaders: Make sure everyone has their *Epic* Church History Timeline chart to use when discussing questions about the time period. Briefly go over the other sections of the chart—especially the Events & Influences section—so that you can situate the story of the Church in the larger story of the world.

B. Learn the Story

Discussion Leaders: Unless there are comments or questions about Steve Weidenkopf's presentation, dive into answering the discussion questions in Section C.

C. Take a Deeper Look

1. *One historian has remarked that Constantine gave the world the vision of what a Christian Emperor could be. What is your assessment of Constantine and his relationship with the Church?*

   Constantine, like all great men and women of history, was a complex individual. On the one hand, he listened to the Lord and responded to the vision he received and initiated favorable policies towards the Church while Emperor. On the other hand, he was seduced by imperial politics and executed his oldest son, issued a series of repressive laws and meddled in the affairs of the Church. Although Constantine called the Council of Nicaea (the decision was approved by the Pope) to settle the Arian dispute, he failed to adequately enforce the teachings of the Council allowing Arianism to regain its strength and afflict the Church for centuries. His meddlesome dealings with the Church set a dangerous precedent that clouded Church-state relations in the East as well as the relationship between the Eastern and Western parts of the Church. Constantine should be remembered and honored for his role in the history of the Church but the full story of his involvement and its effects cannot be understated or forgotten.

2. *The Edict of Milan is one of the most significant events in Church history. When was it issued? What did it accomplish? Why do you think it was important?*

   Constantine and his co-emperor, Licinius, issued the Edict of Milan in the year 313. It granted "free and absolute permission to practice their religion to the Christians," and it ordered the return of confiscated Christian property. However, it did *not* condemn or outlaw paganism, but instead allowed religious liberty for each person to worship, as he desired.

   Its importance is obvious but cannot be overemphasized. After centuries of persecution, where any period of toleration could vanish at a governor's whim, the Church was finally allowed the right of public worship. From the shadowy catacombs to glorious new churches, the faithful increased at amazing rates, and the tenets of Christian morality worked their way into secular laws, planting the seed of the temporal and spiritual endeavor that would become Christendom. Erratically, but steadily, the Church would grow in prestige and power until she became the source of unity for all of Europe. Rough roads still lay ahead, but this was clearly a landmark event in Western civilization that forever changed the course of history.

3. *Arianism plagued the Church for over 300 years. What were the basic tenets of this heresy? Does it still exist today?*

    Arianism taught that only the Father was truly God. There was a time when the Son, Jesus Christ, did not exist, and the Father created him out of nothing. The Son, the first of all creatures, was an intermediary between God and the inferior creatures, and the Holy Spirit was demoted to the second foremost creature. Arianism granted to Jesus "all the divine attributes—except divinity itself."

    The notion that Jesus is not God continues to gain adherents in our modern society. From the Jesus Seminar (a group of "scholars" who deny Christ's divinity and resurrection," among other teachings) to *The Da Vinci Code*, many assert that Jesus was just a nice man. It was Constantine or the Church that made Him into God. The popularity of these teachings should give heed to Christians to double our efforts to explain and defend our Faith by words and deeds.

4. *Popular books and movies often claim that Constantine completely transformed the Church. In particular, it is said that Constantine imposed the idea that Jesus Christ was God and established the hierarchical order of the Church. Can you refute this error based on what you've learned about Church history?*

    Already covered in previous sessions, the writings of St. Clement of Rome and St. Ignatius of Antioch are clear witnesses to the existence of the Church's hierarchy since the very beginning, more than a hundred years before Constantine was even born. It is also clear from the writings of St. Ignatius, St. Irenaeus, and others that the early Christians firmly believed that Jesus Christ was God.

    Perhaps, the most ironic fact is that Constantine did attempt to force his opinion on the Church, but on the opposite side! Constantine did not understand the nuanced position of Arius, and in a misguided attempt to establish unity in the Church; he not only exiled St. Athanasius, Defender of Orthodoxy, but also tried to force the Bishop of Constantinople to receive Arius into the Church. Far from imposing the idea of Jesus as God upon the Church, Constantine actually promoted the heresy that Jesus was not divine!

5. *As Emperor, Constantine was very involved in Church affairs. How do you think that precedent influenced Church history? How do political leaders approach the Church in our modern times? What is the proper role of the Church in politics?*

    Constantine was very involved in Church affairs, much to the detriment of the Church. He appointed bishops and even exiled them when they defended the Faith. He set a dangerous precedent (known as *Caesaro-papism*) of imperial meddling in ecclesiastical affairs that would plague the Church for centuries. One can trace the latent seed for the Great Schism (Eastern Church breaking away from the West) of 1054 to Constantine's misguided involvement.

    Church-state relations comprise a fascinating sub-study within Church history. Many secular rulers were allies of the Church and looked favorably on her. Others were quite malignant and tried to dominate and control the Church in their realms; some even succeeded. Today, the Church and especially the papacy is, for the most part, respected in the international political arena. Political leaders frequently visit Rome to meet with the Holy Father and the Vatican has an active presence at the United Nations as a permanent observer.

    The Church's role in politics is articulated in the *Catechism of the Catholic Church*: "The Church, because of her commission and competence, is not to be confused in any way with the political community. [However,] It is the part of the Church's mission 'to pass moral judgments even in matters related to politics, whenever the fundamental rights of man or the salvation of souls requires it" (Nos. 2245–2246).

6. *The Council of Nicaea was the first Ecumenical Council of the Church. What was the major discussion at the council? The council produced a "negative" and "positive" teaching. What were they?*

Constantine called the Council of Nicaea in the year 325, Pope Sylvester I approved the gathering, and papal legates were present throughout the council. It focused mainly on the Arian heresy. The "negative" teaching consisted in condemning Arius and his erroneous teachings. Positively, the Nicene Creed was drafted to give the Church a statement of the Faith (this is the Creed we say at Mass every Sunday). The word *homoousios* (consubstantial) was used to explain that the Son was of the same *substance* as the Father.

7. *A new form of living the Christian Faith emerged during this time period, monasticism. Where did it originate and why there? With whom? How was it lived?*

One historian has referred to the men who left the world in order to draw deeper into a relationship with Christ as "the athletes of Christ". Through their efforts, the orthodox Faith of Nicaea was preserved, especially in Egypt, the home of Arius. One reason why monasticism originated in Egypt is because of the witness of the martyrs. Christians were heavily persecuted in Egypt during Diocletian's Great Persecution early in the fourth century. This witness produced a flowering of holiness through the life of St. Anthony the Abbot (250–356) and St. Pachomius (290–348). St. Anthony lived an eremitical life. His reputation for holiness grew and he soon attracted a large following. These men all lived as hermits but in close proximity to one another. St. Anthony organized some communal time among the monks but they did not live together in community. St. Pachomius organized monks into a community (known as cenobitic monasticism) and founded several monasteries throughout Egypt. Eventually, St. Basil the Great wrote a rule for how monks were to live in community embracing an active and contemplative lifestyle. Later, St. Benedict in the West would likewise organize the daily life of monks in his rule.

D. Application

Discussion Leaders: If time permits, ask the group members to share their personal responses to the application question.

Christians were finally welcomed into Roman society, but a new host of subtle dangers was waiting for them. The constant threat of persecution had made it easy to stay focused on the Faith, but now the temptation to be "of the world" sapped the zeal of many Catholics. Monasticism responded to this problem. Many choose to leave the world in order to grow closer to Christ in solitude or in community. Are you tempted to be of the world and not just in it? What modern-day distractions keep your heart from resting in Christ? What can you do to most take advantage of the time God has graciously given you?

Close with the prayer found in the Leader's Guide.

Conversion & Councils – Part II

A. Review the Context

Discussion Leaders: Make sure everyone has their *Epic* Church History Timeline chart to use when discussing questions about the time period. Briefly go over the other sections of the chart—especially the Events & Influences section—so that you can situate the story of the Church in the larger story of the world.

B. Learn the Story

Discussion Leaders: Unless there are comments or questions about Steve Weidenkopf's presentation, dive into answering the discussion questions in Section C.

C. Take a Deeper Look

1. *Who was St. Athanasius? Can you describe the important role he played in the story of the Church? Describe the persecution he underwent for the Faith. What made him persevere?*

   St. Athanasius was ordained a deacon in Alexandria, Egypt, about the same time that Arius began preaching his heresy. He faithfully assisted as a secretary at the Council of Nicaea. He was then elected as Bishop of Alexandria in 326, and from this point on his life was filled with adventure. He refused to give in to pressure from the Arians, defending the orthodox teaching from Nicaea at every opportunity. So they launched a smear campaign against him, accusing him of various crimes such as abusing a prostitute, dabbling in black magic, and even murdering a bishop. St. Athanasius's clever defenses are legendary, but they were not enough to keep him from being exiled five times. During all of these hair-raising adventures, St. Athanasius still managed to write numerous treaties on the faith, including the Creed of St. Athanasius. His determination to preserve the True Faith as it was handed on to him, no matter what the cost, has served as an example for Catholics in every generation.

2. *Julian the Apostate persecuted the Church after its legalization. Have you been persecuted for your faith? If so, share that experience.*

   Answers will vary but many Catholics in today's world have suffered ridicule and insults for holding to the Faith. Many may even share stories of how they "persecuted" Christians before their conversion.

3. *After Nicaea, there were three other ecumenical councils during this time period. When and where were they held? What main aspects of the Faith did each council address? Which heresies did each council condemn?*

   The second ecumenical council was called in 381 in the city of Constantinople by the emperor Theodosius. This council reaffirmed the declarations of the Council of Nicaea and further developed teachings on the Holy Spirit. Since the Arian heresy had denied the divinity of the Holy Spirit as well as the Son, the bishops added the phrase, "We believe in the Holy Spirit, the Lord and Life-giver, who proceeds from the Father, who with the Father and Son is worshipped and glorified" to the Nicene Creed. The council was attended only by eastern bishops, and their addition of a canon declaring the

See of Constantinople the second most important (Rome being the first) was not confirmed by the pope because it sought to replace the ancient ordering of Sees—Rome, Alexandria, Antioch.

The third ecumenical council was called in 431 in the city of Ephesus by the emperor Theodosius II. Nestorius, Patriarch of Constantinople, attacked the veneration of the Blessed Virgin Mary as Mother of God, or *Theotokos* on Christmas Day, 428. He taught that there were two natures *and* two persons in Jesus Christ, completely dividing the human person from the divine person. St. Cyril of Alexandria was the primary defender of the orthodox faith, and the council lasted only one day as Nestorius was excommunicated and Mary confirmed as *Theotokos*.

The fourth ecumenical council was called in 451 at Chalcedon. Eutyches, a monk from Constantinople, now went in the opposite direction of Nestorius and declared that Jesus had only one nature. This heresy is known as Monophysitism (one nature) and essentially denies the humanity of Christ. Proponents of the Monophysite heresy hi-jacked a council that met at Ephesus in 449 (forever known as the "Robber's Council"). Pope Leo the Great refused to confirm its decrees. Instead, a new council was called at Chalcedon, and Pope Leo's letter, known as the *Tome of Leo*, declared that Christ is one divine Person with a united divine and human nature (theologically, this is known as the hypostatic union).

4.   *The Roman Empire had persecuted the Church for hundreds of years, and a strong anti-Catholic sentiment thrived amongst the still generally pagan populace who continued to blame warfare on the frontier and natural disasters on Christians. One might guess that Christians would have celebrated the collapse of the Roman Empire, but this was not the case. How can you explain the sadness that many Catholics, like St. Augustine and St. Jerome, expressed when they saw the demise of Rome?*

Answers may vary. Here are two ideas to consider:

1.   Despite the widespread growth of the Christian Faith, Roman culture had remained decadent. After legalization many converts turned to the Faith for reasons of social gain, they had little true devotion and were often as decadent as the pagans. It was a common theme among the Church Fathers to preach that the barbarians were being sent against Christian Rome as a chastisement from God for their sinful ways, much in the way ancient Israel was sent into exile by the Babylonians. Pope St. Leo the Great even called Attila the Hun the "Scourge of God." In seeing the fall of the Roman Empire, many devout Christians saw the divine judgment of God, and their sorrow was an expression of their penitence.

2.   The Church has always recognized authentic civil leaders as endowed with authority by God. Jesus told Pontius Pilate that his authority was given to him from above (John 19:10-11), and St. Paul wrote, during the reign of the mad Emperor Nero, that the state was given certain rights by God including punishment of criminals (Romans 13:1-4). The early apologists, such as Tertullian, encouraged Catholics to be good citizens and even encouraged prayer for the emperor. It was clear that, despite the abuse of power and personal flaws of the emperors, Catholics still realized the importance of sound government in fostering the common good. The early Church Fathers knew that order was always preferable to anarchy, and that it was only through civilization that the Gospel could spread and the Faith could grow.

5.   *Pope St. Leo I is one of the few popes in all of history to be called "Great." What were some of his significant accomplishments? Why do you think he is called "great"? What makes a pope "Great"?*

Pope St. Leo defeated the Monophysite heresy at the Council of Chalcedon (451), and his Tome is a masterful explanation of the Faith in Jesus Christ as fully God and fully Man. Perhaps his most well known accomplishment was his meeting with Attila the Hun in 452. While it is not clear if Attila turned back because he was paid a ransom, because he was short on supplies, or because he was superstitious, the fact is that it was Pope St. Leo's embassy that gave Attila a chance to change his mind. St. Leo saved Rome from another barbarian horde in 455, and while he was unable to keep the Vandals from looting the city he did convince them to leave the inhabitants and ancient monuments unscathed. Considering the Vandals track record, this was an impressive victory. He defended the Primacy of the See of Rome by refusing to approve the extra canon added by Eastern bishops claiming that Constantinople was equal in authority to Rome at the Council of Chalcedon.

There has never been an official definition of what makes a Pope "great." While opinions may vary as to what St. Leo did to merit this great title, here are a few ideas:

1. Pope St. Leo forever changed the way in which the world viewed the papacy. Although the Christian Faith was the official state religion, many powerful pagans were still skeptical and often blamed the barbarian invasions and poor economic state on the fact that Rome had abandoned the pagan gods in favor of Jesus Christ. When St. Leo single-handedly stopped Attila the Hun, he forever changed this perception, showing the pagans that Rome was saved by the vicar of the Christian God.

2. In saving the city of Rome from the Huns and from the full savagery of the Vandals, Pope St. Leo may have saved the entire Church herself. Heresies had consistently plagued the Church in the East, and the Eastern bishops would often cave to pressure from the Emperor. With these problems plaguing the East and the Western Empire in splintering shambles, if the See of Rome had been destroyed the Church would have lost its only source of orthodox and independent authority.

3. The Tome of Leo is a masterwork of theology that explains the mystery of the Incarnation. Not only did the Tome end a potentially devastating heresy it helped to provide the words to understand and explain how Christ can be both God and man. The Council Fathers motivated by Pope St. Leo's Tome wrote, "Our Lord Jesus Christ [is] … to be acknowledged in two natures, without confusion, without change, without division and without separation." Pope St. Leo's influence on theology is greatly significant.

4. Pope St. Leo was the lone great figure during this span of history. During his lifetime there were no great emperors or powerful Church Fathers. Pope St. Leo took up the responsibility of defending the Church from heretics, the state from barbarians, and the poor from famine. Perhaps it is the solitary nature of his Herculean effort that won him the mantle of "Great."

6.   *The baptism of Clovis in 496 is another monumental event in Church History. Why is it important?*

The tribal chiefs that were seizing power all throughout the fallen empire were Arians. They were, for the most part, hostile to the orthodox Catholic Faith, and either persecuted or barely tolerated Catholics in their lands. The exception was Clovis, a pagan barbarian, who came to rule most of what is now France. His conversion not only secured a safe haven in which the Church would grow strong, but it also showed that the Catholic Faith was not simply the stale state religion of a crumbling empire but a universal religion that embraced barbarian warriors as well as Roman nobles. The kingdom of Clovis (modern-day France) would become the homeland of a myriad of holy saints, the site of beautiful cathedrals, and the last line of defense against Muslim and Viking invaders.

D. Application

Discussion Leaders: If time permits, ask the group members to share their personal responses to the application question.

This time period was witness to four important ecumenical councils where the Holy Spirit guided the Pope and bishops to develop the authentic expression of many of our core doctrinal beliefs. These teachings were necessary to settle theological disputes in the Church in order for harmony and unity to reign. Over the centuries many theological works have been written on the teachings first articulated in this time period. Do you make time to study these and other teachings in order to grow closer to Christ and His Church? Are there teachings of the Church you disagree with? Why? Have you read and reflected on why the Church teaches these things?

Close with the prayer found in the Leader's Guide.

E. Wrap-up

1. *What is the color of this time period? How can you remember it?*

   Remember the Conversion & Councils time period by its color, white: a symbol of the empire's conversion as it is clothed white in Christ and of the Holy Spirit guiding the Church through the four ecumenical councils.

2. *What is the main theme of this period?*

   The main theme of the Conversion & Councils period is the conversion of the Roman Empire to the Catholic Faith as well as the conversion of Clovis and the Franks and the development of Church doctrine by the first four ecumenical councils.

3. *Write a one- or two-sentence summary of the Conversion & Councils period in order to recall the main events of Church history during this time.*

   Answers will vary but they should contain most of the main events listed on the *Epic* Church History Timeline chart.

Missionaries & the Emperor – Part I

A. Review the Context

Discussion Leaders: Make sure everyone has their *Epic* Church History Timeline chart to use when discussing questions about the time period. Briefly go over the other sections of the chart—especially the Events & Influences section—so that you can situate the story of the Church in the larger story of the world.

B. Learn the Story

Discussion Leaders: Unless there are comments or questions about Steve Weidenkopf's presentation, dive into answering the discussion questions in Section C.

C. Take a Deeper Look

1. *Why is St. Benedict known as the father of Western monasticism? Explain, in your own words, his vision of monasticism.*

   Although he is not the first monk in Church history, St. Benedict is known as the father of Western Monasticism because he established the rule that would become the foundation for all monasteries in the Western Church. His rule transformed loose and scattered associations of pious Christians into focused, organized, and unified groups that brought great strength to the Church and helped preserve the invaluable written treasures of the ancient world, most especially the Bible.

   While the phrasing will obviously vary as people answer in their own words, here are the basic tenets of St. Benedict's vision for monks:

   - A monk's life should consist of work, prayer, study, self-denial, and, as appropriate, fasting. However, Benedictine monks did not practice extreme poverty, and the Rule guaranteed that all basic needs should be met.

   - A monk should imitate the life of Christ by being devoted to chastity, temperance, and obedience.

   - A monk should spend his life in service to others and be especially concerned with preserving the Sacred Scriptures.

   - An abbot—elected from among the community for life—should lead the monks. The abbot served as a father-figure for the community and would exercise his ministry in imitation of Christ's servant leadership.

2. *Pope St. Gregory I is another of the few popes to be awarded the title of "Great." What were some of his achievements? Does he share anything in common with Pope St. Leo the Great?*

   As the head of the Catholic Church, Pope St. Gregory removed and disciplined corrupt clergy, enforced priestly celibacy, defended the Church from heresies, rebuked John the Faster, patriarch of Constantinople, when he usurped the title of "ecumenical patriarch," ensured the conversion of Britain, revitalized the liturgy, preserved the tombs of the saints, and wrote several major theological works, as well as over 800 letters. As the chief civil administrator of Rome, he fended off the Lombards, sometimes by bribes and other times by force, established hospitals and orphanages, rebuilt many of the great buildings, protected Jews from persecution, and organized the distribution of food to the poor.

Although their pontificates were more than 100 years apart, there are several striking similarities between St. Gregory the Great and St. Leo the Great. Both defended Rome from invasion. Both rigorously reformed the Church, fought heresies, and enforced the authority of the pope over the Eastern Church (remember, St. Leo refused to approve of the final canon from the Council of Chalcedon which was slipped in by Eastern bishops in an attempt to gain power equal to that of Rome for the See of Constantinople). Both wrote masterpieces of theology. Both figures stood alone during a time when there were few if any other "great men." Perhaps most significantly both changed the way in which the world viewed the papacy with St. Leo showing pagans that it was the Vicar of Christ that saved them from doom and St. Gregory showing that a pope could provide for the physical as well as spiritual needs of the people.

3. *Despite the many difficulties of this time period, missionary activity thrived. Who were some of the great missionaries that conquered hearts for Christ? What procedures did they follow in bringing the Light of Christ to others?*

St. Augustine of Canterbury was the head missionary sent by Pope St. Gregory the Great to convert the Angles of Britain. He landed in England in 597 and met with King Ethelbert of Kent who was very receptive to the Faith. The missionaries made such quick progress that there were 10,000 baptisms on Christmas Day of that same year.

In the sixth century, Irish monk-missionaries, such as St. Columba and St. Brendan, sailed to Scotland, Wales, Brittany, Iceland, and possibly even America spreading the Faith and bringing people into the Church.

Pope St. Gregory the Great provided guidance to St. Augustine on how to deal with certain issues when evangelizing pagans. This guidance centered on respecting the sacred places, customs and festivals of the pagans. Christian missionaries were instructed to accommodate these customs and festivals as long as they did not contradict the Faith. Additionally, they re-used pagan worship sites now consecrated to the One True God. Pope St. Gregory the Great recognized that authentic conversion requires time and effort that cannot be forced. The basic procedures outline by Pope St. Gregory shaped Catholic missionary efforts throughout Church history.

4. *One way to learn about a religion is to learn about its founder. If someone wants to understand the Christian Faith, he must obviously study the life and teachings of Jesus Christ just as he would have to study about Buddha in order to learn about Buddhism. What has learning about the life of Mohammed taught you about Islam?*

Each person may have a different response. In order to foster discussion, here is a recap of some of the historical facts about Mohammed covered in the *Epic* lecture:

- Mohammed received his first revelations in 610, and he initially believed he was possessed by evil spirits and even contemplated suicide.

- In 624, Mohammed led his followers to attack a caravan during a pagan holy month in which it was forbidden to shed blood. He explained his actions by a "revelation" justifying the attack.

- Mohammed was a militant warrior, who personally engaged in twenty-seven battles.

- He had fourteen wives, his favorite being only nine years old (he married her when she was six and he was in his fifties).

- He took his own daughter-in-law as a wife after he received a "revelation" explaining it was Allah's will.

- Mohammed was merciless to those who opposed him.

  - He ordered assassinations on political and personal opponents, including a mother of five, who had written unfavorable things about him.

  - He ordered the beheading of over 500 Jews in Medina on trumped up charges of collaboration with the Meccans (who were besieging Medina)

- He showed great contempt for the Jewish people. He claimed "revelations" from Allah that justified the expulsion and killing of all Jews.

  - He is recorded as saying, "The last hour would not come unless the Muslims will fight against the Jews, and the Muslims would kill them until the Jews would hide themselves behind a stone or a tree and a stone or a tree would say: Muslim, or the servant of Allah, there is a Jew behind me; come and kill him."

- Mohammed died in 632. In his farewell address, he told his followers to "*fight* all men until they say 'there is no god but Allah'" (emphasis added).

5. *What was life like for a non-Muslim in areas that had been conquered by Islam?*

A non-Muslim who survived the initial sack of the city or town was granted second-class status. Non-Muslims were forced to wear special clothing that indicated their status, and in some cases they were even branded with special marks. In order to maintain *dhimmih* status, which meant they were "protected," non-Muslims had to pay a tax known as the *jizya*. The paying of the tax itself required an embarrassing ritual where the Muslim would collect the money from the infidel while holding his beard and striking him across the face. No one was exempt from the tax, not widows, orphans, or even the dead. Public expression of the Catholic Faith was forbidden, and any expression of allegiance to a non-Muslim power resulted in forfeiture of "protected" status. Non-Muslims were not allowed to erect or restore any non-Muslim place of worship, and things such as crosses and church bells were considered contraband. Non-Muslims were not even allowed to give testimony in court. Many non-Muslims were sold into slavery, and castrating slaves became a popular way of providing suitable guards for Muslim harems. Although forced conversion to Islam was rare, there was heavy societal pressure to convert because of the second-class status afforded to non-Muslim members of Islamic society.

6. *What happened to Mohammed's followers after his death? How does this compare with the story of the early Christians?*

Following Mohammed's final command to "fight all men until they say there is no god but Allah," the early Muslims, through a series of savage victories, conquered Syria in 635, Persia in 637, Jerusalem in 638, Egypt in 642, all of North Africa by the year 700, the entire Iberian peninsula (Spain) by 711 and had infiltrated Gaul to within 120 miles of Paris by 732. Muslim armies even raided the Italian mainland, plundering Rome in 846. They burned St. Benedict's historic monastery at Monte Cassino in 884 and had conquered Sicily by 878. Their forays into Italy were not stopped until the early tenth century when Pope John X led an army against them and secured a great victory.

Christ exhorted his disciples to love their enemies. In contrast with Muslim practice, the early Christians—who were persecuted by the Roman Empire—instead of participating in conquest or violence, actually prayed for the emperor and their persecutors. Rather than convert the world by the sword, the Church miraculously grew in numbers and strength despite widespread oppression.

D. Application

Discussion Leaders: If time permits, ask the group members to share their personal responses to the application question.

Since its beginnings in the seventh century, Islam has had a profound impact on the Church and Western civilization. Our modern world continues to feel its impact. Over the centuries, missionary efforts to Muslim nations have not borne much fruit. Why do you think that is the case? In what ways can you help spread the message of Gospel to Muslims today?

Close with the prayer found in the Leader's Guide.

Missionaries & the Emperor – Part II

A. Review the Context

Discussion Leaders: Make sure everyone has their *Epic* Church History Timeline chart to use when discussing questions about the time period. Briefly go over the other sections of the chart—especially the Events & Influences section—so that you can situate the story of the Church in the larger story of the world.

B. Learn the Story

Discussion Leaders: Unless there are comments or questions about Steve Weidenkopf's presentation, dive into answering the discussion questions in Section C.

C. Take a Deeper Look

1. *France has traditionally been known as the "Eldest Daughter of the Church." Why?*

    Beginning with the baptism of King Clovis at the end of the fifth century, France has always had a unique relationship with the Church—sometimes good and sometimes bad, but always unique and extremely important. During this time period, several events occur that further solidify the unique bond between France and the Church. Specifically, the reign of Pepin establishes the link between the pope and the kings of the Franks and culminates in the creation of the Papal States (modern-day Vatican City is all that remains of the pope's temporal holdings, which once encompassed most of modern-day Italy). The bond grows stronger during the rule of Charlemagne who protects the pope and is crowned Holy Roman Emperor. Charlemagne sponsored missionary activity and was very conscious of his duty to spread the Gospel. We will see that the relationship between the Church and France will continue to grow and develop—sometimes in negative as well as in positive ways throughout the remaining time periods.

2. *Charlemagne is considered one of the most important figures in Western Civilization. What have you learned about him? Who do you think was a more significant Christian ruler, Constantine or Charlemagne?*

    Charlemagne was the son of Pepin and the grandson of Charles Martel. He was the greatest Western leader in centuries and was able to unify Europe and protect her borders from would-be invaders such as the Basques, the Muslims, and the Saxons. He became King of the Franks in 771 and was crowned as the first Holy Roman Emperor by Pope Leo III on Christmas Day in the year 800. He was very pious, attending daily Mass and vespers, and he had an earnest desire to protect the Church and especially the pope from all enemies. He worked hard to improve education throughout his land, founding many schools, and he undertook an extensive revival of the arts and architecture which is known as the Carolingian Renaissance.

    As to who is the more significant ruler, opinions vary. While Charlemagne was the epitome of a Christian emperor, he fulfilled and improved the model that was established and made possible by Constantine. He did not, though, meddle in ecclesiastical affairs like Constantine. Both figures have great strengths and weaknesses, and both struggled to improve the lives and faith of their subjects.

There is, however, one basic fact that cannot be denied: Western civilization owes a tremendous debt to both of these great men.

3. *Many modern critics accuse Charlemagne of being a tyrant because he forced the Saxons to convert to the Christian Faith. Can you explain the actual circumstances surrounding this event? Do you agree with the critics? Why or why not?*

The Saxons were a tribe of pagan barbarians who practiced human sacrifice and ritual cannibalism. They would cross the Frankish border to loot and terrorize, and Charlemagne struggled with them for thirty years. Negotiated treaties with the Saxons were only a temporary relief, as they would slide back into their violent ways within a few years. Charlemagne did not force conversion on any other peoples that he conquered, and it was only after a particularly fierce revolt that he finally lost patience with the Saxons. The Saxon leader was baptized in 785, and strict laws were established enforcing conversion to maintain peace and prevent the Saxons from reverting to their pagan practices.

Opinions regarding these laws may vary. The Church has never condoned forced conversion, and one is certainly free to disagree with Charlemagne's course of action. However, given that this was clearly the exception to the norm and an exception made only because of the particularly fierce and violent nature of the Saxons, it is difficult to argue that Charlemagne was a "tyrant" or that he acted out of bad intentions. Regardless of whether one agrees or disagrees with his choice, it would certainly be a mistake to let this one act overshadow the tremendous contributions Charlemagne made to Western civilization.

4. *The Photian Schism was yet another step along the path that eventually led to the Great Schism where the Eastern Church broke away from the Catholic Church. Can you explain what happened?*

Through political maneuvering Photius, a laymen, was named the patriarch of Constantinople. The Byzantine emperor exiled St. Ignatius, the actual patriarch, while Photius sent a preemptive letter to Pope St. Nicholas the Great claiming that St. Ignatius had abandoned his post. The pope saw through the ploy and sent a legate to investigate, but the legate was lavishly bribed and sided with Photius. St. Ignatius, finally released from captivity, appealed directly to Pope St. Nicholas, but the emperor ignored the pope's rebuke and claimed that he, not Rome, held total control over the Church in Constantinople. In 867 Photius "anathematized" Pope St. Nicholas, but in 869, after the reigning Byzantine emperor died, the Fourth Council of Constantinople excommunicated Photius, and St. Ignatius was restored. Photius was later reconciled to the Church and, after St. Ignatius's death, became the legitimate patriarch of Constantinople. However, he immediately lapsed into his old habits and was again excommunicated.

5. *What was the heresy of Iconoclasm? Which Doctor of the Church was one of its chief opponents?*

Iconoclasm, which is derived from the Greek for "image breaking," consisted of a complete rejection of all religious images as idolatrous. It originates from the influence of Islam's rejection of all graven images and resurfaces centuries later in the acts and teachings of the Protestant revolutionaries. Byzantine emperor Leo III initiated it when he blamed a devastating volcanic eruption on God venting his wrath against people "worshipping" images of Jesus, Mary, and the saints. St. John Damascene, the "Doctor of Christian Art," was the most notable defender of the orthodox practice of iconography, and his work was directly cited at the Second Council of Nicaea (787), which condemned iconoclasm and defined the proper categories of worship and veneration: *latria* (worship given to God alone), *dulia* (reverence for the saints), and *hyperdulia* (special reverence given to the Blessed Virgin Mary).

6. *The ninth and tenth centuries are often called the "Dark Ages." What happened in the Church and Europe during this time period to warrant such a title?*

Although somewhat of a misnomer, there were certainly dark times for the Church and Western civilization during this time period. The ninth and tenth centuries particularly stand out because of the collapse of the Carolingian empire and the rise of the Vikings. Unfortunately, the peace and security established by Charlemagne did not continue upon his death. His empire was divided among his three sons and his future descendants did not receive his gift of leadership and good administration.

The Vikings began their savage raiding toward the latter half of the eighth century. Their raids culminated in the middle of the ninth century with a daring strike up the Seine at Paris on Easter Sunday. The Vikings burned, pillaged, and raped all throughout Western Europe. Their destructive behavior caused havoc and terror, which caused a stagnation of culture and learning to such an extent that it almost became extinct. One historian has noted that European culture and civilization made it through this time by "the skin of our teeth."

Finally, the Church and the papacy, established by Christ to be a bulwark of truth and a beacon of hope in the world, suffered through a lack of strong leadership. The life expectancy of popes during this time period was less than a year. Several were gruesomely murdered or simply "disappeared." The local secular rulers vied for control of the papacy and made a mockery of the institution. This is clearly illustrated in the bizarre "Synod of the Corpse" where the decayed corpse of Pope Formosus was put on trial by his successor Pope Stephen VII.

7. *The foundation of the monastery at Cluny is one of the most significant events in the history of the Church and Western civilization. Why was it important?*

The genius of Cluny was its independence. The organizational structure of the monastery was revolutionary for its time. Wishing to ensure the monastery stayed free of local ecclesiastical politics and lackluster practice of the Faith, William of Aquitaine made Cluny beholden only to the pope and not the local bishop. This move ensured that Cluny could become a center of authentic monastic renewal. The reform of monastic life begun at Cluny would spread throughout the Church and would encompass even the papacy as three monks of Cluny would become noted papal reformers in the eleventh century.

D. Application

Discussion Leaders: If time permits, ask the group members to share their personal responses to the application question.

This time period clearly illustrates that the Catholic Church saved Western civilization. Through the dedicated studiousness of monks, thousands of ancient manuscripts and classics of literature were preserved. Charlemagne's emphasis on education and art not only saved but also built up the patrimony of Western Civilization. Today, through art museums, libraries, and the Internet we have access to more cultural riches of the past than any generation before us. In what ways have you endeavored to appreciate and learn the classics of Western civilization? How can you grow in your appreciation for the Catholic heritage that has been handed down to you?

Close with the prayer found in the Leader's Guide.

E. Wrap-up

1. *What is the color of this time period? How can you remember it?*

   Remember the Missionaries & the Emperor time period by its color, purple: it represents the royalty of the first Holy Roman emperor, Charlemagne.

2. *What is the main theme of this period?*

   The main theme of the Missionaries & the Emperor period is the spreading of the Light of Christ and the preservation of Western Civilization through an age of darkness thanks to the work of the Church and the Holy Roman emperor, Charlemagne.

3. *Write a one- or two-sentence summary of the Missionaries & the Emperor period in order to recall the main events of Church history during this time.*

   Answers will vary but they should contain most of the main events listed on the *Epic* Church History Timeline chart.

Crusaders and Scholars – Part I

A. Review the Context

Discussion Leaders: Make sure everyone has their *Epic* Church History Timeline chart to use when discussing questions about the time period. Briefly go over the other sections of the chart—especially the Events & Influences section—so that you can situate the story of the Church in the larger story of the world.

B. Learn the Story

Discussion Leaders: Unless there are comments or questions about Steve Weidenkopf's presentation, dive into answering the discussion questions in Section C.

C. Take a Deeper Look

1. *The mid to late eleventh century was one of reform in the Church and papacy in particular. What reforms were instituted? By whom? Why was reform necessary?*

   By the middle of the eleventh century the Church was in need of serious reforms. Many ecclesiastical abuses had become commonplace, including simony, the buying and selling of Church offices, and violations of celibacy, including homosexuality. The reform movement was centered at Cluny and its reforming influence spread throughout the Church culminating in the pontificates of two of its former members, Pope St. Gregory VII and Pope Bl. Urban II.

   One important reform was promulgated by Pope Nicholas II but was the brainchild of the Cluniac monk Hildebrand (later Pope Gregory VII), the election of the pope by the college of cardinals. Before this reform, the Pope was elected by a wide variety of measures (including popular acclamation and election by the Holy Roman Emperor). This measure allowed the papacy to gain a level of independence from secular rulers. The eighth, ninth, and early tenth centuries are full of the stories of meddlesome secular rulers displacing and installing popes of their choosing. This practice continued at the local level in Germany with Henry IV who advocated the secular ruler's right to invest bishops with not only their temporal but also spiritual symbols of office. The "Investiture Controversy" was a crucial time in the history of the Church and the strength of Pope St. Gregory VII ensured the Church would not easily become the plaything of secular princes.

   These reforms along with the strong pontificates of St. Leo IX, St. Gregory VII and Bl. Urban II helped to firmly establish an independent papacy at the service of the universal Church. These men also undertook the arduous task of cleaning the Church from the accumulated vices of her clergy. Over time, through their tireless efforts, the Church would emerge healthier and stronger.

2. *The Great Schism of 1054 rent the Church of Christ asunder; a wound that unfortunately, continues into our own times. What happened during this momentous event? How can this wound be healed?*

   Tension between East and West had been brewing for centuries. Many events transpired which paved the way for the sad event known as the Great Schism. Although there were a few legitimate theological issues, the separation came about through the clash of personalities and the maneuverings of politics. In 1043, Michael Cerularius was appointed Patriarch of Constantinople. Cerularius outlawed the celebration of the Latin-rite form of the Mass in Constantinople in 1052, angering the large Latin community in the city. When Pope St. Leo IX heard of this event, he sent a letter to the Patriarch and the Emperor and then decided to follow the letter with a papal embassy. Chosen to lead the official delegation was Cardinal Humbert, a very learned man who also was quite hot-tempered. While the delegation was in transit to the East, Pope St. Leo IX undertook battle against the Normans who had conquered Sicily and made their way up mainland Italy. Fearful that the papacy would lose its independence and once again become the prize of strong secular rulers, Pope St. Leo IX raised an army. Defeated in the field, Pope St. Leo IX's worst nightmare becomes reality as the Normans hold him prisoner. His captivity and the delay in communications due to the great distance are significant factors in the Great Schism.

Cardinal Humbert's embassy did not bring reconciliation but further obstinacy. Unable to reach an agreement, Cardinal Humbert drafts a bull of excommunication and with dramatic flair walks into St. Sophia (the cathedral of the patriarch) and places the bull on the middle of the main altar. It is important to recall the fact that Cardinal Humbert overstepped his mandate in issuing the bull of excommunication. Nonetheless, the damage had been done. Patriarch Cerularius issued his own bull of excommunication of the Pope and the Great Schism had arrived.

Although there were brief times of reconciliation (the last in the fifteenth century), the Eastern and Western Churches have remained apart. Nothing theologically stands in the way of reunification, just age-old prejudices. Pope Paul VI and Patriarch Athenagoras officially lifted the mutual excommunications in 1965. Reunification was at the top of Pope John Paul II's agenda. He even described the rift as a serious wound that made the Church breathe with only one lung. Benedict XVI has continued the efforts of John Paul II and one can pray and hope that the Holy Spirit may move both sides closer in order that Christ's mandate may be achieved.

3. *Pope Bl. Urban II introduced a revolutionary idea into the life of Christendom at the end of the eleventh century. What was that idea? What did it lead to?*

At the local council of Clermont in November 1095, Pope Bl. Urban II called the First Crusade. His predecessor Pope St. Gregory VII had planned to call for the formation of an army of Western knights to help the besieged Eastern Christians but was unable to solidify his plans. Urban II's revolutionary idea was not in calling the crusade but rather in choosing its goal. Urban focused the goal of the crusade on the liberation of Jerusalem specifically and aiding the Eastern Christians secondary. He also articulated the notion that warfare was a penitential act akin to fasting, praying, and almsgiving. This notion allowed for warriors to utilize their profession in a penitential way on an armed pilgrimage (pilgrimages before this time were strictly unarmed affairs). This radical idea gave laymen an understanding that they could participate in the universal call to holiness through the exercise of their vocation as warriors rather than by joining a monastery or the clergy. His idea spawned the crusading movement, which would occupy 700 years of European and Church history.

4. *The preaching of the First Crusade drew an enormous response. Why do you think people went on crusade? What motivated them? If you had lived at the end of the eleventh century what would have been your response?*

It is estimated that 100,000 people responded to Urban's call to crusade to Jerusalem. Not all were warriors (about 60,000); among them were the poor and elderly, women and children. Although a decision to "take the cross" was an individual one, there are many reasons why people desired to go to the Holy Land. This was a time of intense interest in pilgrimages. Rome, Jerusalem, and Santiago de Compostela were popular places of pilgrimage. Pope Bl. Urban II made this pilgrimage to Jerusalem very attractive for people of Faith by promising a plenary indulgence for the temporal punishment due to sin whose guilt had already been forgiven in the sacrament of confession. Although it was (and in some cases continues to be) posited that crusaders went to the Holy Land in order to get rich through plunder and booty, a great wealth of modern scholarship has revealed this thought to be erroneous. The study of medieval charters (legal documents most akin to our real estates title documents) indicates that vast majority of crusaders were motivated not by greed but by love of Christ and concern for the salvation of their souls.

5. *The First Crusade was the one truly successful crusade. How did it succeed and why? The crusaders were certain God was with them while they marched to Jerusalem, what events transpired to solidify this certainty?*

The goal of the First Crusade was the liberation of Jerusalem from the hands of the Muslims. The crusaders accomplished this goal in July 1099, three years after they left France. Of the eight traditionally numbered crusades, this was the only one to achieve its stated goal. There are many reasons for the success of this crusade, chief among them was the political situation in the Holy Land itself. The Muslim world was disjointed, and the main rulers frequently warred against one another. The Seljuk Turks controlled Anatolia, Syria, and Palestine; they were Sunni Muslims aligned with the Abbasid caliphate headquartered in Baghdad. The Fatimids, who were Shi'ite Muslims, controlled Egypt and held influence over the southern end of the Holy Land. They even swept into Palestine in 1098 and conquered Jerusalem while the crusaders were encamped at Antioch. Muslim disunity prevented the outnumbered crusaders from being driven into the sea. Additionally, the Muslims had not encountered heavily armored knights before (although they did battle heavily armed Frankish cavalry in the eighth century) and were not familiar with European tactics. The crusaders attributed their success to a series of miraculous events at opportune times throughout the march to Jerusalem. Chief among them was the finding of the Holy Lance (the lance used by St. Longinus to pierce the side of Our Lord on the Cross) at Antioch when the situation was desperate. The finding of the Holy Lance significantly improved morale and shortly thereafter, the crusaders defeated a Muslim force outside the walls. Contemporary chronicles record the appearance of angels and the spirits of deceased crusaders joining the army in battle.

The First Crusade was on the verge of disaster several times during the course of its pilgrimage to the Holy City but each time the crusade was saved. The crusaders attributed these events to the intercession of the Lord and a sure sign to them that He was with them and blessed their campaign.

D. Application

Discussion Leaders: If time permits, ask the group members to share their personal responses to the application question.

The Crusades are one of the most misunderstood events in Western history. Many modern myths have been perpetuated for so long that it is difficult to separate fact from fiction in our minds—despite the recent scholarship that is at odds with the popular stories. What were you impressions of the crusades before listening to this presentation? Have they changed? If confronted by someone about the Crusades and the Church, how would you respond?

Close with the prayer found in the Leader's Guide.

Crusaders and Scholars – Part II

A. Review the Context

Discussion Leaders: Make sure everyone has their *Epic* Church History Timeline chart to use when discussing questions about the time period. Briefly go over the other sections of the chart—especially the Events & Influences section—so that you can situate the story of the Church in the larger story of the world.

B. Learn the Story

Discussion Leaders: Unless there are comments or questions about Steve Weidenkopf's presentation, dive into answering the discussion questions in Section C.

C. Take a Deeper Look

1. *Many modern myths surround the crusades including the "massacre of Jerusalem" where it is alleged that the crusaders massacred all the inhabitants of the city upon its liberation. The story goes that so much blood was spilled the crusaders waded through it up to their knees. What is the true story of the liberation of Jerusalem?*

The crusaders arrived outside the walls of Jerusalem in June 1099. They had been three years on the march and had sustained a very high casualty rate (only 12,000 of the 60,000 fighting men were left). They had conducted two sieges (Nicaea and Antioch), fought many battles, and suffered through agonizing heat. Their ability to besiege the city successfully was greatly in doubt. After several attempts to breach the defense had failed, a priest was given a vision of the late Bishop Adhemar, Pope Bl. Urban II's representative and nominal head of the expedition. The spirit of Bishop Adhemar scolded the lords for their infighting and told the army that if they marched penitentially (barefoot and unarmed) around the city, it would fall to them in nine days. The crusaders did as instructed, and nine days later, on July 15, 1099, they entered the city. Conventional rules of warfare in force at the time dictated no mercy for the inhabitants of a city who tried to outlast a siege. The victors were accorded the spoils of war. In the case of Jerusalem, a good portion of the inhabitants had left the city before the siege, and many who did not were captured and ransomed; nonetheless, once in the city, many crusaders acted in barbarous fashion and there was much bloodshed. The notion that so much blood was spilled that it was "up to their knees" is, of course, physically impossible and hyperbole. The liberation of Jerusalem serves as a reminder that, although most of the crusaders undertook the armed pilgrimage for pious reasons, not all acted with piety throughout the crusade.

2. *One historian has remarked, "The Second Crusade was born by papal pronouncement, but it drew breath from the words of Bernard of Clairvaux." Who was St. Bernard and what role did he play in the Second Crusade?*

St. Bernard of Clairvaux (1090–1153) was one of the most brilliant minds of the Church. He was well known during his lifetime, and he exercised an enormous influence in the affairs of the Church during the early twelfth century. A member of the reform-minded Cistercians, St. Bernard was chosen to lead the first "daughter house" from the main abbey at Cîteaux. At the beginning of his tenure there were only twelve monks at this new abbey in Clairvaux, but there were 700 at the time of his death. St. Bernard was a scholarly man who wrote many theological works, commentaries on Scripture, and even prayers (he is the author of the *Memorare*). St. Bernard also debated the theological agitator Peter Abelard, a well-known professor of the time who enjoyed pushing the envelope of conventional theological and philosophical thinking to its heretical limit.

Pope Bl. Eugenius III called the Second Crusade in response to the fall of Edessa, the first crusader state. St. Bernard and his Cistercian brothers traveled throughout western Europe preaching the crusade and motivating warriors to join the campaign. St. Bernard personally convinced the Holy Roman emperor, Conrad III, to join the crusade with his warriors. His preaching at the emperor's court elicited such a large response that he was forced to tear cloth from his own habit to give to those who vowed to "take the cross" to the Holy Land. Additionally, St. Bernard was influential in the approval of the Templar military religious community. He wrote the Templar rule and encouraged warriors to join the community. A holy and influential man, St. Bernard is one of the magnificent figures of this time period who played a profound role in the history of the Church.

3. *Although hopes were high, the Second Crusade was not as successful as the First. What happened on this crusade? Who were the main participants? Why did it fail?*

The Second Crusade was led by two of the most important kings of Europe at the time—Conrad III, Holy Roman emperor and king of the Germans, and Louis VII, king of France. Its goal was to re-take the city of Edessa and re-establish the northernmost crusader state. Unfortunately, the kings did not coordinate their plans; this fact, coupled with the unfriendly attitude of the Byzantines, doomed the crusade. Conrad III led his army through the difficult terrain of Anatolia, where he was ambushed and suffered a devastating defeat. Louis VII tried the coastal road but was constantly harassed and had to ask the Byzantines for naval transports. The Byzantines did not arrive with enough transports for his army, so Louis was forced to leave the bulk of his troops to fend for themselves. They were picked to pieces on the march and very few actually made it to Antioch. At a council of war, Louis and Conrad decided to piece together an army with the remaining soldiers, some local forces, and newly-arrived crusaders. They were persuaded by the local nobles to abandon plans to re-take Edessa and instead march to Damascus. They arrived at Damascus and encamped in a strategic location to begin the siege, but their army was not large enough to completely encircle the city. As a result, scores of Muslim reinforcements were able to come to the aid of the defenders. Conrad and Louis decided to break camp and move to a location closer to the main route of the arriving reinforcements in an effort to stem the flow. Unfortunately, they picked a poorly defensible area with no access to food or water. The situation soon proved desperate, and the crusaders were forced to abandon the siege after only four days. Conrad III left soon after for home, but Louis VII stayed in the Holy Land for some time afterwards in order to help solidify the Christian position.

4. *The recent movie* Kingdom of Heaven *(2005; directed by Ridley Scott, starring Orlando Bloom, Jeremy Irons and Liam Neeson) purports to tell the story of the Kingdom of Jerusalem right before the Third Crusade. Have you seen this movie? If so, share your thoughts on this film. Are the real historical events portrayed accurately?*

Although entertaining at times, the movie *Kingdom of Heaven* is a huge disappointment. It illustrates the popular misconceptions of the crusades. Set before the Third Crusade, the movie tells the story of the Kingdom of Jerusalem and the rise of Saladin, culminating with the Muslim siege of Jerusalem in 1187. The main character is based on an historical person, Balian of Ibelin (played by Orlando Bloom) and the movie revolves around his pilgrimage to Jerusalem, where he takes over the estate of his father in Ibelin. Balian is portrayed as a courageous yet conflicted (especially about his faith) knight—a far cry from the historical Balian. Some characters are portrayed with a certain level of historical authenticity (with a dramatic flair, of course), such as Reynald de Châtillon and Guy de Lusignan. However, the movie's underlying main theme is that religion is bad because it causes people to engage in violence. No attempt is made to portray the crusaders in light of the time period; rather, the modern myths of the crusades are perpetuated—i.e., that the crusaders were bloodthirsty barbarians who came to the East to destroy and conquer the peace-loving, well-educated, and cultured Muslims. The well-respected crusade historian, Jonathan Riley-Smith sums it up best when he writes that the movie is "rubbish, ridiculous, complete fiction" and gives "Osama bin Laden's version of history."

5. *The Third Crusade is probably the most well-known crusade. It is a dramatic story with larger than life characters. Who were the main actors in this great story? What happened during this crusade? Was it successful?*

The Third Crusade, called after the Muslims conquered Jerusalem, is sometimes called the "Three Kings Crusade" because the three main monarchs of Europe participated.

The Holy Roman emperor, Frederick Barbarossa, gathered a large army and marched overland to Constantinople. While in Anatolia, his army was harassed by Byzantine forces (the Emperor Isaac II had made a secret treaty with Saladin to try and prevent the crusaders from reaching the Holy Land). Even though the crusaders were short on provisions, morale was high, especially after winning a battle against the Turks. Unfortunately, disaster struck when the aged emperor drowned while crossing a river. The loss of their revered leader overwhelmed the Germans, and most returned home.

France and England had been at war when Jerusalem fell. Pope Gregory VIII's crusade promulgation mandated a seven-year truce throughout Christendom so that Christian warriors would be free from internal affairs to fight in the Holy Land. Once the peace treaty was signed, Philip II Augustus, King of France, and Richard I the Lionheart, King of England, made plans to go on the crusade. Although they took separate routes to the Holy Land, Philip and Richard continued to squabble with one another. Philip arrived in the East first and marshalled his army to assist in the siege of the city of Acre (which King Guy had besieged for two years). Richard arrived a bit later and was instrumental in concluding the siege and capturing the city. Annoyed at Richard's success and deviously planning to capture Richard's French holdings, Philip II left the crusade and returned home.

Last among the three kings, Richard spends the next year shoring up crusader defenses, engaging Saladin in battle (which he wins), and dealing with a political crisis in the kingdom. He is unable to mount a successful assault on Jerusalem and instead settles for a peace treaty with Saladin that gave the Christians unhindered access to the city for three years. Many of Richard's knights take advantage of the truce to visit the Holy City and complete their pilgrimage; Richard refuses, since his mission was to recapture the city, which he had failed to do. Plagued by reports of Philip's moves on his French holdings and the evil doings of his brother John, Richard breaks camp and returns west.

The Third Crusade was full of promise and looked as if it would mimic the success of the First Crusade. Unfortunately, bickering between Philip and Richard as well as the accidental drowning of Frederick Barbarossa doomed the crusade.

6. *Pope Innocent III was one of the most influential popes in Church history. How did Innocent influence the Church and Western civilization?*

Innocent was the youngest man elected to the chair of Peter in more than 150 years. Only thirty-seven at the time of his election, Innocent was a well-known and respected scholar. He was very determined to ensure the independence of the papacy and his first papal address he stressed the supremacy of the spiritual realm over the temporal realm. He stated that the pope possesses the fullness of spiritual power and is a moral judge over secular rulers. He brought a series of innovations to the crusading movement, shaping it for centuries. Particularly, he advocated an active role for the Church's organization and administration of future crusades; however, his vision did not translate well in reality as the disastrous Fourth Crusade illustrated. He changed the financial structure of crusading; previously, crusade expenses were borne by the individual crusader (although both Philip and Richard levied a general tax on their subjects, known as the "Saladin tithe"). Innocent levied a general tax against the clergy to help pay the costs of crusading. He also expanded the notion of crusading and shifted its focus from the East to the West by calling the Albigensian crusade in southern France. Finally, he changed the understanding of a crusade as an armed pilgrimage to a period of military service. Previously, one "took the cross" and went on an armed pilgrimage. In order to receive the crusader indulgence, one had to complete the pilgrimage. Innocent granted the crusader indulgence to those who provided military service for a period of time (forty days). Finally, Innocent also changed an earlier prohibition against crusading. Bl. Urban II mandated that a married man could crusade only if his wife gave her permission. This prohibition was borne out of a desire to respect the obligations of marriage and to ensure the safety and protection of a man's wife and family. Innocent abolished this prohibition principally because men began to use the prohibition as an excuse not to crusade!

Innocent also called the Fourth Lateran Council where the Albigensian heresy was condemned and numerous reform decrees were promulgated. This Council also instituted the "Easter Duty," by which Catholics are required to receive the sacraments of Holy Eucharist and penance at least once a year, preferably during the Easter season.

Innocent shaped the future of the Church and Western civilization by approving the establishment of the Order of Friars Minor (the Franciscans) in 1210. Innocent approved the Franciscans after a dream in which he saw his cathedral (the Basilica of St. John Lateran) leaning, swaying, and ready to collapse. Innocent then saw a little man run up and set his shoulder against the building and it straightened and stood firm. When he met St. Francis he recognized him as the little man from his dream.

7. *One historian has remarked that the "conquest of Constantinople is one of those events that can be explained but not justified." Explain what happened during the Fourth Crusade. How has it affected the Church?*

The Fourth Crusade is perhaps the darkest event in the history of the crusading movement. Originally envisioned and called by Pope Innocent III, the Fourth Crusade was launched to conquer Egypt in order to use it as a base of operations for launching a successful attack on the Holy Land and the recapturing of Jerusalem. Unfortunately, the crusade was doomed from the beginning. The crusade was in need of naval transport, so a group of nobles traveled to Venice to contract for ships. The plan called for each crusader to pay his own transportation costs. Unfortunately, when time came to embark the ships, less than half the required number of crusaders arrived in Venice. The crusaders could not pay the Venetians the money they owed. Stuck in such a bad situation, the Venetian leader, Enrico Dandolo, devised a plan where the crusaders would help Venice capture the Christian city of Zara as payment of their debt. Although ordered by Pope Innocent III to not attack Zara, the crusaders did not listen and captured the city. While encamped in Zara, Alexius Angelus, an exiled Byzantine prince arrived with an enticing proposition. Alexius' father, Emperor Isaac II, had been deposed and blinded by his own brother, who took the throne as Alexius III. Alexius Angelus asked the crusaders to help him overthrow his uncle and place him on the throne. In return, he promised to unite the Byzantine Church with Rome, join the crusade with 10,000 men, permanently maintain 500 knights in the Holy Land, and pay the crusaders 200,000 silver marks. Once again, Pope Innocent III cajoled, implored, and threatened the crusaders not to deviate from the goal of the Holy Land; once again, they did not listen. The crusaders took Alexius Angelus and Constantinople, but instead of an expected warm welcome, the people of the city pelted Alexius with trash and shouted insults. The crusaders were forced with the prospect of besieging the greatest and most well-defended city in the world. After the crusaders attacked, Alexius III panicked and fled the city. Alexius Angelus was then installed as Alexius IV.

The crusade rank and file believed they had finished their work and were eager to depart for the Holy Land. However, the nobles wanted payment from Alexius IV, who was only able to accumulate half the payment. In order to deliver the remaining amount, he took precious jewels from icons and other sacred objects, which infuriated the people and they turned on him. Eventually, he was imprisoned and killed by his trusted lieutenant who took the throne for himself (Alexius V). The crusaders were greatly upset at the death of Alexius IV and endeavored to punish the usurper by conquering the city. The crusaders successfully breached the defenses and poured into the city, sacking it for three days. The sack was especially brutal and great sacrilege was committed. Many of the city's precious art, artifacts and relics were transported west. The crusaders set up the Latin Empire of Constantinople, which lasted until 1261.

The sack of Constantinople severely damaged the relationship between East and West. Despite Pope Innocent's protestations, Easterners still consider the pope ultimately responsible for the destruction of the city. This mood was evidenced by the reaction to Pope John Paul II's visit to Athens in 1996. Lining his motorcade route were Orthodox monks holding signs with the year "1204" (the year of the sack) written on them.

8. *The Fifth Crusade was on the verge of great success when it ended in bitter defeat. Why did this crusade fail? A very important visitor arrived in the crusader camp, who and why was he there?*

Pope Innocent III learned from the mistakes of the Fourth Crusade and endeavored to ensure those same mistakes would not be repeated. At the Fourth Lateran Council plans were laid for another crusade to the East. This affair was to be completely managed and administered by the Church—in the hopes that the whims of secular rulers would not dictate the course of the crusade as had happened during the Fourth Crusade. Cardinal Pelagius was appointed leader and the crusade set sail for Egypt in 1218. They besieged the strategically important city of Damietta. The sultan of Egypt, al-Kamil, offered to return crusader land in Palestine and a thirty-year truce in return for the crusaders withdrawal. The military orders argued against accepting such a deal and Cardinal Pelagius tendered the official "no." The crusaders had been in Egypt for over a year when a very famous and important person visited their camp—St. Francis of Assisi. St. Francis was technically not a crusader since he did not "take the cross," but he came to Egypt on a mission of conversion. He endeavored boldly to attempt the conversion of Sultan al-Kamil. St. Francis and a companion made their way to the Muslim lines and were brought to al-Kamil, who responded warmly and listened courteously to St. Francis. In the end, though, the sultan told Francis that he could not accept the Christian faith due to cultural and political reasons. He did ask the holy beggar to pray for him so that God may make known to him which belief is more pleasing, Islam or Christianity.

D. Application

Discussion Leaders: If time permits, ask the group members to share their personal responses to the application question.

Western Crusaders, against the explicit orders of Pope Innocent III, sacked the great imperial city of Constantinople in 1204. This one event has negatively shaped East/West relations for the last 800 years. Despite the efforts of Pope John Paul II and Pope Benedict XVI, the Church remains disunited. In what ways can you help bring about a level of respect and understanding between East and West? Why should the Church and individual Catholics work for reunification?

Close with the prayer found in the Leader's Guide.

Crusaders and Scholars – Part III

A. Review the Context

Discussion Leaders: Make sure everyone has their *Epic* Church History Timeline chart to use when discussing questions about the time period. Briefly go over the other sections of the chart especially the Events & Influences section so that you can situate the story of the Church in the larger story of the world.

B. Learn the Story

Discussion Leaders: Unless there are comments or questions about Steve Weidenkopf's presentation, dive into answering the discussion questions in Section C.

C. Take a Deeper Look

1. *The relationship between Church and state has, at times, been quite tenuous. During this time period, England becomes the battleground between Church and state. What happened? How was the conflict resolved?*

   Henry II, the Plantagenet king of England, never went on crusade but he was intimately related to those who did. His grandfather was Fulk of Anjou, King of Jerusalem from 1131–1143 and his wife; Eleanor of Aquitaine who was a participant of the Second Crusade, accompanying her then husband, Louis VII of France. Henry was a strong-willed king who desired total control in his realm. He believed he had been handed a marvelous chance to control the Church in England when the archbishop of Canterbury died in 1162. His plan was to appoint his trusted friend and advisor Thomas Becket as archbishop of Canterbury. Henry miscalculated his friend's response. Thrust into such a prominent ecclesiastical role, Becket responded with a profound and sincere conversion and endeavored to protect the Church and her clergy from the excesses of the king. Clergy members who committed crimes in England were tried in Church courts rather than royal courts, a practice Henry did not like. Henry tried to have this practice changed. His proposal met with the strong resistance of Becket. The personal feud escalated to such an extent that Becket, fearing for his life, was forced to leave England in the dark of night and escape to France. Eventually, Becket returned but continued to uphold the independence of the Church. One night while campaigning in France, Henry flew into a rage and yelled at a group of his knights asking why no one would free him from this meddlesome priest. These knights took the words of the king to heart and journeyed to Canterbury where they martyred Becket in his cathedral on December 29, 1170.

   Several years later, Henry was forced to undergo public penance for his role in Becket's martyrdom. Through the witness of St. Thomas Becket, the Church in England was able to maintain her independence from the crown, at least for the time being.

2. *The history of the Church and Western civilization were profoundly influenced by the arrival of Sts. Francis and Dominic. Who were these holy men? What impact did they have on the Church and the world? Who is your favorite and why?*

   The thirteenth century witnessed an intense period of spiritual activity with the arrival of Sts. Francis and Dominic. Francis was born into a wealthy Italian family and became a soldier at the age of twenty.

Suffering from an illness, Francis had a dream where he saw a house full of armor marked with crosses. Another dream followed in which Christ told him to serve God rather than man. Later, Francis stopped to pray at the church of San Damiano, where he saw Christ on the crucifix come alive and tell him to "go and repair my Church." Francis initially took the saying literally and began repairing the little church. Eventually, Francis understood the call in a more universal sense. He renounces his wealth and embraces "Sister Poverty." His holiness attracted others, and he established the Order of Friars Minor, a religious community dedicated to preaching, serving the poor and begging for their sustenance. The community grew rapidly, and was formally approved by Pope Innocent III in 1210. The Franciscans have given the Church several great theologians (including St. Bonaventure) and four popes, as well as centuries of great service spreading the Gospel.

St. Dominic of Castile came into contact with the Albigensian heretics while traveling with his bishop. He realized the success of the heresy was partially caused by the inability of the clergy to mount an effective verbal offensive against the errors. Linked to this problem was the fact the vast majority of people did not know their Faith, primarily because there was no one qualified to teach them. He founded the Order of Preachers (the Dominicans) to combat this problem. Like Francis, Dominic wished his brothers to live through begging imitating the humble simplicity of Christ. The Dominicans were approved by Pope Honorius III in 1216 and were given a universal preaching mission. Their primary apostolate continues to be an intellectual one focused on the studying and teaching of philosophy and theology. Like the Franciscans, the Dominicans have given the Church several great theologians (chief among them St. Thomas Aquinas) and four popes.

3. *One historian calls Frederick II "the crusader without Faith." Who was Frederick II? What was his relationship with the Church?*

By the age of four, Frederick's parents, Emperor Henry VI and Constance of Sicily, had died and Pope Innocent III assumed legal guardianship of the young man. Despite the guardianship, Frederick was an avowed agnostic who ridiculed the Christian faith, kept a Muslim bodyguard, quarreled with the papacy, and attempted to exercise absolute control over the Church in his lands. Contemporaries called him *stupor mundi*, "the astonishment of the world," because they were amazed at his outspokenness against the Faith and his friendliness towards Muslims.

Frederick followed in the footsteps of his famous grandfather, Frederick Barbarossa, when he "took the cross" during his coronation as king of the Germans in 1215. Due to political considerations, he repeatedly stalled going on crusade and was partly blamed for the failure of the Fifth Crusade, since he had promised multiple times to set out with his army but never did. Pope Gregory IX demanded that Frederick fulfill his vow in 1227 (twelve years after his profession). After promising to do so but then reneging, Gregory had excommunicated him. In complete disregard of the papal pronouncement, Frederick finally decided to go on a crusade. Since he was excommunicated, his campaign was not technically a crusade and was not sanctioned by the Church. He arrived in the Holy Land in 1228 and opened negotiations with al-Kamil leading to a treaty signed in 1229. The treaty gave Christians control of Jerusalem (except for the Temple area and the Dome of the Rock) for ten years in exchange for Frederick's agreement not to support any Christian war against Muslims.

Frederick's remaining years as Holy Roman emperor were marked by constant struggle with the Church. He wrote letters denying Christ established a unique and special role on St. Peter and his successors; instead Peter was merely a spokesman for the apostles. After his second excommunication by Gregory IX, he expelled all Franciscans and Dominicans from his territory and appointed bishops without papal consent. He invaded the Papal States in 1240 capturing and executing several relatives of Gregory IX. As a result, Gregory IX proclaimed a crusade against Frederick, as did his successor Innocent IV. The thirteenth ecumenical council, the First Council of Lyons (1245), was called to address Frederick and his antics. The council officially deposed him as Holy Roman emperor and decreed his excommunication. Frederick died in 1250 and was buried in a red silk robe bearing Arabic inscriptions.

4. *In contrast to Frederick II, King St. Louis IX of France is called the "Perfect Crusader." Who was St. Louis IX? Why is he considered the "perfect crusader"?*

St. Louis IX was a handsome, charitable man and a loving husband and father. He was one of the greatest kings of France, governing his land justly for forty-four years. Louis was an excellent general with an excellent military mind. He was a skilled tactician and a leader of men. Louis' family was steeped in the crusading movement: his great-great-great grandfather's brother participated in the First Crusade; his great-grandfather, Louis VII, was one of the leaders of the Second Crusade; his grandfather, Philip, II participated in the Third Crusade; and his father, Louis VIII, fought in southern France during the Albigensian Crusade. Louis considered crusading a kingly and chivalrous duty. Several years after the treaty of Frederick II expired in 1239, the Egyptians once again conquered Palestine capturing Jerusalem and slaughtering the Christian community in the city. When the news of this event reached Europe, Louis "took the cross" and made plans to go to the Holy Land. He used enormous amounts of the royal revenue to pay for the logistical necessities of the crusade. The army arrived in Egypt and quickly conquered Damietta. Advancing on Cairo, his brother altered Louis' plans and disaster ensued. Louis' brother and a large contingent of knights were killed and the main force under Louis was surrounded and eventually forced to surrender. Louis and many of the nobles were imprisoned and held for ransom. After a month in captivity, Louis was released after paying the ransom. He allowed his troops to go home if they wished, but he decided to make sail for Palestine. He stayed in the Holy Land for four years where he provided solid leadership for the Kingdom of Jerusalem and helped to solidify its defenses.

St. Louis would crusade once more before the end of his life. This time he led an ill-fated campaign to North Africa where disease broke out in camp. The papal legate, Louis's son and Louis himself all perished. St. Louis' last words were "Jerusalem, Jerusalem." A saintly man who ruled as king imitating the servant leadership of Christ, St. Louis IX is the "perfect crusader" because he crusaded for pure motives; love of Christ, the Church and the Holy Land.

5. *What is heresy? What are its effects on the Church and society?*

The *Catechism* No. 2089 defines heresy, as "the obstinate post-baptismal denial of some truth which must be believed with divine and catholic faith." Heresy is a dangerous thing not only for the Church but also for the individual. Heresy threatens the unity of the Church and sows division and conflict. In the thirteenth century, heresy was also seen as a great threat to society. Most heretical movements ushered in periods of unrest and violence and secular rulers were quick to restore order. The Church is also concerned about heresy because it endangers the soul of the individual who holds to such false beliefs. The Church, continuing the salvific mission of Christ, desires the salvation of all and is therefore in charity must admonish heretics to return to the Faith through confession and penance.

6. *The Church launched a crusade against the Albigensian heretics in southern France in the thirteenth century. What were the beliefs of the Albigensians? How was the heresy eradicated?*

Although the Albigensian movement arose in southern France in the thirteenth century, its teachings stretch back to the time of ancient Greece. The Albigensians were essentially Gnostics, an ancient heresy that held a dualist worldview. They believed there were a god of light and a god of darkness who were continually at war with one another. The god of light created all good things, which are spiritual. The god of darkness created all evil things, which are material. Therefore, a person's soul is good but a person's body is evil. This fundamental belief leads to the rejection of, among other things, the

Incarnation, the Eucharist, and marriage. The Albigensians established a counter-Church, complete with a hierarchy and ritual worship. The leaders of the movement, known as the "perfect," took part in a ritual known as the *consolamentum*, which they also administered. A "perfect" was required to undergo rigorous fasting, abstain from sexual intercourse, and refrain from eating meat and eggs. The highest form of worship was suicide, the releasing of the "good" spirit from the "evil" body.

Although a crusade was called against them, the Albigensians were not eradicated as a result of armed conflict. Rather, the heresy died out by the establishment of the Inquisition. Over a period of time, the Inquisition helped restore peace by helping the heretics return to the Faith through confession and penance.

7. *Like the crusades, the "Inquisition" is one of the most misunderstood and maligned events in Church history. Explain the creation of the medieval inquisitors. Describe the procedures used by these inquisitors. Were they just?*

Pope Gregory IX formally established the Inquisition in 1231 to restore peace, unity and the Faith to southern France as a result of the Albigensian heresy. The inquisitors would arrive in a location, announce their presence and institute a thirty-day "self incrimination period" known as the "term of grace." Anyone who had heretical beliefs could come before the inquisitors and incriminate themselves, asking for pardon. A suitable and not harsh penance was given after which the heretic was welcomed back into the fold. After the thirty-days, the Inquisition would take accusations from others. The accused was brought before the inquisitors, given an opportunity to list all real or perceived enemies, whose testimony was not used at the trial. The accused was interviewed by the inquisitors, witnesses were called and the accused given multiple opportunities to repent. Although popular imagery links cruel and extreme torture with the Inquisition, the reality is that torture was not authorized for use until 1252, although it was a staple in the secular courts. Torture was always considered an optional tool at the disposal of the inquisitors and one of the most influential inquisitors and author of a manual for inquisitors, Bernardo Gui, disliked using torture. Torture was never used as a form of punishment, only as a means to elicit information. Inquisitorial procedure called for the use of torture once and only after every other method to gain information had been utilized. All sentences were reviewed by a panel of clergy and lay men and sent to the diocesan bishop. Punishments ranged from light to severe forms of penance, including going on pilgrimage or crusade. If a person was obstinate in his or her refusal to repent after numerous opportunities, then the Inquisition handed the person over to the secular courts for violation of secular law (for heresy was considered a secular crime as well as an ecclesiastical one). It was the state, never the Church, that then condemned a person to death for heretical beliefs and carried out the sentence. Recent scholarship has shown convincingly the procedures used by the Inquisition were more just and humane than the secular courts of the time. As with all human institutions, there were abuses but in most cases the abusers were dealt with promptly and removed from office.

8. *What is scholasticism? Who were the main proponents? What was its effect?*

Scholasticism is a method and a system of learning with the investigation of knowledge as the prime goal. As a system, scholasticism sought to integrate theology, philosophy, and Sacred Scripture. St. Anselm of Canterbury (1037–1109) is considered the father of scholasticism. St. Anselm believed that faith and reason are harmonious, and he began the integration of Aristotelian philosophy and theology. He wrote works on why God became man and devised a proof for the existence of God. Perhaps the most influential and famous scholastics were St. Bonaventure (1221–1274) and St. Thomas Aquinas (1225–1274). Bonaventure was concerned with synthesizing theology, philosophy, and mysticism. He left the academic world to become minister general of the Franciscans. St. Thomas Aquinas was a Dominican who studied under St. Albert the Great. His masterpiece, the *Summa Theologica*, is the epitome of scholasticism. Besides theological masterpieces, St. Thomas wrote Eucharistic hymns such as *Tantum Ergo*. The effects of scholasticism are still felt today, not only in the Church but also in Western society. Scholastic works are still read at universities throughout the world. The intense intellectual activity of the thirteenth century continues to inspire, educate, and appeal to people nearly eight hundred years later.

D. Application

Discussion Leaders: If time permits, ask the group members to share their personal responses to the application question.

The Church responded to the heretics in southern France in a variety of ways. Preaching and even fighting were utilized with little success. It was only the process of the Inquisition that restored unity and peace to the Church and society. When confronted by those who believe differently than you, how do you respond? Share an experience in which you defended the Faith to a person who had great animosity to the Church. How can the events of Church history help us to defend the Faith when the time arrives?

Close with the prayer found in the Leader's Guide.

E. Wrap-up

1. *What is the color of this time period? How can you remember it?*

   Remember the Crusaders and Scholars time period by its color, navy blue: it represents the land of France where the majority of crusaders originated as well as where many scholastics studied, wrote and taught.

2. *What is the main theme of this period?*

   The main theme of the Crusaders and Scholars period is the glory of Christendom reflected in intense activity in the military, spiritual and intellectual spheres.

3. *Write a one- or two-sentence summary of the Missionaries & the Emperor period in order to recall the main events of Church History during this time.*

   Answers will vary but they should contain most of the main events listed on the *Epic* Church History Timeline chart.

Weak Leaders & Schism – Part I

A. Review the Context

Discussion Leaders: Make sure everyone has their *Epic* Church History Timeline chart to use when discussing questions about the time period. Briefly go over the other sections of the chart especially the Events & Influences section so that you can situate the story of the Church in the larger story of the world.

B. Learn the Story

Discussion Leaders: Unless there are comments or questions about Steve Weidenkopf's presentation, dive into answering the discussion questions in Section C.

C. Take a Deeper Look

1. *Who was St. Celestine V and what role did he play in the epic story of the Church?*

   Pope Nicolas IV died in 1292 and two years later no successor had been elected. The papacy, unfortunately, had become a prize in the insidious game of power politics. Charles II, king of Naples and grandson of St. Louis IX, came to Rome in 1293 and urged the cardinals to end their bickering and jockeying and elect a pope. Unable to reach a consensus, the conclave continued. On his way home, King Charles stopped to meet with a hermit known for his sanctity, Peter Murrone. Peter was an eighty-year-old hermit who had lived in a solitary mountain cell for forty years. In the summer of 1294, he wrote a letter to the cardinal bishop of Ostia imploring the cardinals to promptly elect a pope for the good of the Church. The cardinal read Peter's letter in the conclave, recounted Peter's life and holiness and announced he was voting for Peter to be pope. A majority of cardinals followed suit and, without his knowledge, Peter Murrone was elected to the Chair of St. Peter. A short while later, a large procession of cardinals and other dignitaries made their way up the mountain to Peter's cell. Told his election was God's will and desirous to avoid a schism, Peter agreed to his election and took the name Celestine V. Peter lived in Naples, never setting foot in Rome. He quickly realized he lacked the temporal skills to rule as pope and resigned after five months in office. Boniface VIII succeeded him.

2. *Pope Boniface VIII is a controversial figure in Church history. Many historians see his papacy in a negative light believing he is responsible for the weakening of the papacy and the rise of nationalism. Others believe he was a pope who had good intentions but his uncharitable and undiplomatic demeanor caused his ineffectiveness. Who was Boniface VIII? Who did he quarrel with? What is your judgment of his papacy?*

   Boniface VIII was sixty-years old when he was elected pope. He desired to make the papacy stronger in the face of serious secular challenges to the papacy and the independence of the Church. He quarreled with King Philip IV ("the Fair") of France and King Edward I ("the Longshanks") of England. His chief conflict with these monarchs involved taxes. Both Philip and Edward illicitly took funds from the Church to finance their wars. Boniface issued the bull, *Clericis laicos*, directly addressing this problem with strong and at times polemical language. Unfortunately, a few years later, Philip escalated the drama by arrested Boniface's legate in France and accused him of fomenting insurrection against the crown. Furious at this attack on his legate, Boniface issued another bull, *Ausculta fili*, whose opening words were, "Listen, son!" In this bull he threatened Philip with excommunication. Philip responded by burning the bull and declaring anyone who supported the pope to be an enemy of the crown. Boniface issued another more direct bull, *Unam Sanctam*, where he clearly and directly states there are two powers, the spiritual and temporal, and the greater of these is the spiritual. The spiritual can judge the temporal, and only God can judge the spiritual power (namely the pope). In this bull, Boniface threw down the gauntlet at Philip IV, who gladly used the opportunity to strike out. Philip's chief advisor, William of Nogaret, led a group of armed men and captured Boniface. While in custody, Boniface was physically assaulted. He was later freed by townspeople who came to his rescue. Suffering from the effects of the assault, Boniface died a month later.

Boniface had good intentions and tried to strengthen the papacy, but the manner in which he pursued these goals proved his undoing and ultimately wounded the papacy and the Church gravely. Whatever judgment is passed on Boniface, it is clear his papacy marks the end of an era. The secular rulers of Christendom no longer seriously took into account the papacy or the Faith in their public life. Clement V was elected to replace Boniface VIII and it was he who gravely wounded the papacy and began the fracturing process in Christendom by moving the papacy to France.

3. *For seventy-two years the pope lived in Avignon. What led to this relocation of the papacy? What brought the pope back to Rome?*

After the death of Boniface VIII, Philip IV used his power and influence to control the new pope, the Frenchman Clement V. Philip eventually "convinced" Clement to move to Avignon, where the popes would reside for the next seventy-two years.

God used St. Catherine of Siena to bring the papacy back to Rome. She wrote many letters to the pope, full of affection and respect but also exhorting him to embrace his office and his duty and calling him to return to Rome. Gregory XI finally heeded the strong exhortation of St. Catherine and moved the papacy back to its home in 1378.

4. *How did people react to the Black Death? What were some of its long-term effects?*

The bubonic plague, known also as the Black Death, ravaged Europe from 1347 to 1351. Many groups blamed the Jews for causing the plague, and persecution broke out in various regions. Appalled at this behavior, Pope Clement VI quickly threatened to excommunicate anyone harassing Jews on account of the plague.

Some of the long-term effects of the Black Death, other than a substantial decrease in population, included a weakening of the Church through the death of many slow-to-be-replaced bishops and priests, as well as a great decline in the educational system as the number of universities in Europe dwindled from thirty in 1348 to ten in 1400.

5. *The Great Western Schism is perhaps one of the most confusing events in papal history. What caused the schism? Who were the true popes? How was the Schism resolved?*

The Great Western Schism began because of Urban VI's abusive ways and the national politics at work in the college of cardinals (i.e., French vs. Italian cardinals). Even though they had freely elected Urban VI, the cardinals (mostly French) claimed they had been forced by the Roman mob to elect Urban. The schism began when they elected one of their own as the anti-pope Clement VII. The later election of a third anti-pope, Alexander V, resulted from more misguided cardinals who attempted to end the schism by deposing both papal claimants and electing a new "pope." The schism was finally resolved at the Council of Constance which was given approval, and thus authority, by the true Pope, Gregory XII. The council deposed the two antipopes, and, for the good of the Church, Pope Gregory resigned. The Council elected a new pope, Martin V and finally, after almost forty years, the schism was over. Unfortunately, significant damage to the prestige of the papacy and the unity of the Church and Christendom was caused by this bizarre and confusing event.

The true line of popes is:

- Urban VI (1378–1389)
- Boniface IX (1389–1404)
- Innocent VII (1404–1406)
- Gregory XII (1406–1415)
- Martin V (1417–1431)

6. *What was the heresy of conciliarism?*

The heresy of conciliarism was the belief that an ecumenical council—rather than the pope—holds supreme authority in the Church. This heresy grew out of the confusing time of the Great Western Schism. It is exemplified at the "council" of Pisa where cardinals attempted to end the schism on their own initiative without the approval of the pope. Although condemned definitively by the Fifth Lateran Council (1512–1517), this heresy is occasionally present in our own times, especially by those who urge the calling of another council in order to change certain teachings of the Church.

D. Application

Discussion Leaders: If time permits, ask the group members to share their personal responses to the application question.

During this time period the Black Death ravaged Europe, killing men, women, and children by the thousands. Despite the great risk to their own lives, priests and religious rushed to bring the comfort of Christ to the sick. We must approach all things with the virtue of prudence, but there are times when we are called to take a chance or even make some sacrifices. Are you willing to sacrifice your own welfare to bring Christ to those in need? What can you risk for the good of another?

Close with the prayer found in the Leader's Guide.

Session 12 – Responses

Weak Leaders & Schism – Part II

A. Review the Context

Discussion Leaders: Make sure everyone has their *Epic* Church History Timeline chart to use when discussing questions about the time period. Briefly go over the other sections of the chart especially the Events & Influences section so that you can situate the story of the Church in the larger story of the world.

B. Learn the Story

Discussion Leaders: Unless there are comments or questions about Steve Weidenkopf's presentation, dive into answering the discussion questions in Section C.

C. Take a Deeper Look

1. *The Council of Constance (1414–1418) was one of the most important ecumenical councils in Church history. What happened at this council?*

    Called by Holy Roman Emperor Sigismund (1410–1437) principally to end the Great Western Schism, the council also dealt with Jan Hus and his heretical teachings. A large gathering of almost 100,000 people descended on the imperial city in what is now Switzerland. The council deposed both antipopes, Benedict XIII and John XXIII, and received approval from Pope Gregory XII, who also resigned. Martin V was elected, and the scandalous schism came to an end. The effects of the schism, though, would continue and play a leading role in the development of the Protestant revolution.

    Jan Hus was given safe conduct to the council to answer charges of heresy. Although Hus rightly preached against the excesses and corruption of many clergy members in his homeland, he went too far by embracing several heretical teachings of the English heretic John Wyclif. Asked to recant his heretical beliefs, Hus refused. His writings were condemned, and since he remained obstinate in his heresy, he was remanded to the imperial authorities, which sentenced him to death (in violation of his safe conduct). Hus was given multiple opportunities to recant his beliefs and refused on each instance to do so. He also displayed a flippant and arrogant attitude towards the council fathers. Nonetheless, his death was cruel and led to a very bloody fifteen year conflict in Bohemia.

2. *Who were John Wyclif and Jan Hus? What were some of their teachings?*

    John Wyclif was an English heretic who taught at Oxford. He claimed, among other things, that the pope could err and his office was not necessary for the governance of the Church; the Church did not have a right to own property; oral confession of sins was not necessary; transubstantiation did not occur; sacraments administered by a priest in a state of mortal sin were ineffective; the state was superior to the Church; Scripture was the sole authoritative source of divine revelation; veneration of the saints was wrong; prayer for the dead was superfluous; and predestination overrode man's free will. He was investigated by university authorities for his teachings and dismissed from his teaching position. Pope Gregory XI condemned his teachings as heretical in 1377.

    Jan Hus was a heretic from Bohemia and was greatly influenced by Wyclif. He preached against the corruption of the Church in Bohemia, which was a legitimate complaint, but he also called for "reform" of the Church based on the teachings of Wyclif. Hus asserted that Sacred Tradition was not an element of the deposit of faith, and he insisted Christ did not establish the Petrine office. This naturally led to his rejection of the pope's universal jurisdiction and authority over the whole Church. He was tried and condemned at the Council of Constance. After rejecting multiple pleas for him to repudiate his errors, he was handed over to the secular authorities who carried out his execution.

These men are considered "proto-Protestants," since many of their ideas would influence Luther, Calvin, and other Protestant revolutionaries.

3. *Joan of Arc is one of the most captivating characters in all of Church history, but many modern critics and filmmakers paint her in an unfavorable light. What do you know about her story? Can you think of any myths about her? How can you defend her from these modern myths?*

Discussion may vary as people recall different facts about St. Joan of Arc's life. Thanks to the grand scope of her achievements, her popularity, trial and rehabilitation, she is perhaps the most well documented human being to have lived during this time period! There is a standard list of attacks made against St. Joan of Arc by modern critics. What follows are thoughts that can be used to rebut a few of these errors.

Myth: She did not hear heavenly voices but was instead suffering from psychological delusions. The skeptical and brilliant theologians at Poitiers, the battle-hardened soldiers who served under her, and even many of the witnesses and judges at her trial were all convinced by the genius of St. Joan. King Charles VII entrusted his entire army to a seventeen-year-old girl, an amazing event in itself! It is absurd to think that so many would have placed their whole hope in someone who was clearly delusional. There are many well-documented cases of locutions and visitations from heavenly beings throughout Church History both before and after Joan. It is entirely possible and highly probable that Joan's voices were authentic and she was in no way suffering from psychological delusions.

Myth: She was not chaste. Seeing the depths to which her enemies were willing to stoop in order to bring about her condemnation at the trial in Rouen, if there were any evidence showing that she had violated the rule of chastity it would undoubtedly have been used to strengthen their case against her. Interestingly, this point was made by one of the very theologians who participated in her conviction during her posthumous rehabilitation.

Myth: St. Joan of Arc was a feminist. St. Joan did not fight for feminism, and numerous attempts to annex her image or story for feminism is an abuse of history. St. Joan did not achieve her strength by carrying a sword, dressing like a man, or leading armies. Rather she, like all saintly women, achieved her greatness by submitting her will to God's will.

4. *The fall of Constantinople shocked Christendom, and yet nobody answered the pope's call for a new crusade. How do you explain this lackluster response?*

One reason that there was such little interest in a new crusade was that kings had become preoccupied with national affairs and were more concerned about building up their own power rather than defending Christendom. If Turks distracted the Holy Roman Emperor on his Eastern border, then his position among the other nations of Europe would be considerably weaker. Also, the faith of kings had grown tepid, and they could not be motivated by promises of indulgences and other spiritual favors, as had their counterparts in the High Middle Ages.

Another reason that the call may have gone unanswered is that the political influence of the pope was all but non-existent. After Pope Boniface VIII's dealings with King Philip IV, the Avignon papacy, the Great Western Schism, and the rise of conciliarism, the papacy had lost a great deal of prestige and credibility.

5. *What are some of the embarrassing facts about Alexander VI? A non-Catholic may cite these as reasons why the Catholic Church cannot be the one, true Church. How would you respond?*

Among various charges, it is clear that Alexander VI was guilty of pluralism through which he accumulated great wealth by presiding over five separate dioceses. He also fathered numerous illegitimate children while a cardinal and very likely fathered another while pope. He acknowledged his children publicly and failed to rebuke them when their behavior was inappropriate. His son Caesar terrorized the Italian countryside in violent outbursts and was never stopped or rebuked by his father.

Not everything Alexander did was immoral (for example, he cracked down on crime in Rome and presided over a very successful Holy Year in 1500), but his reputation did irreparable damage to the prestige of the papacy. Although Alexander VI and other Renaissance popes led immoral lives, before and during their reigns, it is important to keep in mind that they never taught erroneously on the Faith. Thus, while their example was poor, their teachings on faith and morals were orthodox; a clear witness to the reality of the Holy Spirit, who protected the Church from error during this difficult time of weak leaders and schism. Also, we must remember that immorality does not result in loss of authority. One can cite the examples of St. Peter, who even after denying the Lord retained his position as head of the apostles, the Pharisees, who despite being renounced by Christ for their poor example were still to be obeyed (Matthew 23:1-3), and King David, who remained God's ordained King of Israel even after committing adultery and murder.

6. *Explain the differences between the Spanish Inquisition and the medieval inquisitors? What are some of the widely accepted myths about the Spanish Inquisition? Can you explain the real story of the Inquisition?*

A key distinction to make between the Spanish and medieval Inquisition is that the medieval Inquisition was a papally-created institution administered by Dominicans whose task was to maintain peace and unity throughout the Church. The Spanish Inquisition was a creation of the Spanish crown and established primarily for national security reasons to unify the state.

Popular culture views the Spanish Inquisition as the quintessential example of Catholic intolerance and abuse of power. It is viewed as an unjust system that actively persecuted non-Catholics, forcing them to convert under pain of torture, and often condemned innocent men to painful deaths. From Monty Python and Mel Brooks to even modern-day school textbooks, these baseless myths are widely accepted and often used to embarrass Catholics and attack the Church.

The reality of the Inquisition is that it was a fair and just court that held jurisdiction only over Catholics. Muslims and Jews were never actively persecuted, and only those who converted to the Catholic Faith under false pretenses (known as the converses), were sought for judgment. The process was always formal and relied upon the collection and presentation of evidence. Torture was rarely used (much less than in secular courts at the time), and it was never used as a means to convert people to the Catholic Faith. The Church did not have any authority to sentence people to death, and thus it was actually the secular government that would execute those who were declared obstinate in their heresy. Even those who were executed made up a much smaller number than those executed in modern-day penal systems. A modern scholar of the Spanish Inquisition estimates that over the length of the Inquisition (250 years) approximately 3,000 people were sentenced by the state to capital punishment, an average of twelve per year.

7. *Who was Savonarola?*

Savonarola (1452–1496) was a Dominican monk in Florence who preached against political and religious corruption, angering the powerful de Medici family and Pope Alexander VI. Savonarola was a reformer of sorts but delved into radical avenues that caused his downfall. A severe critic of the Renaissance, which he saw as the glorification of man at the expense of God, he instituted the "bonfire of the vanities" where numerous items considered materialistic and vain were thrown in huge bonfires. His fiery rhetoric at first attracted followers but eventually led to a loss of support. Defying a papal order to stop preaching, as well as a summons to Rome, Savonarola was excommunicated. His brief reign of power and influence came to an end when he was arrested, tried, and condemned for heresy (in reality, he was a schismatic) and handed over to the secular authorities who executed him.

D. Application

Discussion Leaders: If time permits, ask the group members to share their personal responses to the application question.

There are many spiritual benefits from studying Church history. Perhaps the greatest benefit is a deeper appreciation, love, and trust in the Holy Spirit. Reviewing the history of the Church and the papacy, especially during this time period, helps one to realize the Holy Spirit truly animates, guides and preserves the Church in good and bad times. What is your relationship with the Holy Spirit? Do you pray specifically to the Holy Spirit? How can you deepen your understanding of the Third Person of the Holy Trinity?

Close with the prayer found in the Leader's Guide.

E. Wrap-up

1. *What is the color of this time period? How can you remember it?*

   Remember the Weak Leaders & Schism time period by its color, black: it is associated with strife, divisions, setbacks, and death.

2. *What is the main theme of this period?*

   The main theme of the Weak Leaders & Schism period is how weak leadership hurt the Church and brought about schism, laying the groundwork for the Protestant Revolt.

3. *Write a one- or two-sentence summary of the Weak Leaders & Schism period in order to recall the main events of Church history during this time.*

   Answers will vary but they should contain most of the main events listed on the *Epic* Church History Timeline chart.

Protestors & Defenders – Part I

A. Review the Context

Discussion Leaders: Make sure everyone has their *Epic* Church History Timeline chart to use when discussing questions about the time period. Briefly go over the other sections of the chart especially the Events & Influences section so that you can situate the story of the Church in the larger story of the world.

B. Learn the Story

Discussion Leaders: Unless there are comments or questions about Steve Weidenkopf's presentation, dive into answering the discussion questions in Section C.

C. Take a Deeper Look

1. *Pope Julius II is sometimes referred to as the "warrior Pope." Who was this pope and in what ways did he contribute to Western civilization?*

   Guiliano della Rovere was crowned pope on November 28, 1503, taking the name Julius II. Julius ascended the Chair of St. Peter during a very difficult time in the history of the papacy. French meddling in Italy threatened the security and independence of the pope and his temporal possessions. In order to provide long-term security and independence, Julius raised an army and went on campaign. He eventually secured the Papal States against foreign meddling for the next several centuries.

   Julius II was also the Pope who brought the Swiss Guards to Rome. He originally requested the Swiss Diet provide him with 200 mercenaries to be established as a permanent corps in Rome.

   Pope Julius II was not only a warrior but also a patron and lover of Renaissance art and architecture. He commissioned several magnificent works of art and architecture, including Raphael's frescos in the Papal apartments and the building of St. Peter's Basilica. He is perhaps most known for his commissioning of Michelangelo to paint the Sistine Chapel. Their relationship is masterfully illustrated in the 1965 film *The Agony and the Ecstasy*, starring Charlton Heston (as Michelangelo) and Rex Harrison (as Julius II).

2. *The sixteenth century event that shattered the unity of the Church is usually referred to as the Protestant Reformation. Was this event a reformation or a revolution? What's the difference?*

   Although commonly referred as the Protestant Reformation, the events of the sixteenth century (especially in Germany and Switzerland) are more akin to a revolution. Luther advocated the complete destruction of the papacy, the sacramental system, and the understanding of divine revelation. A study of Luther's writings clearly indicates his goal was not to reform the Church but to destroy it and replace it with something entirely different, which is the essence of revolution. A reformation seeks to reform something from within, to make it better. A revolution seeks to destroy and replace the old with something new and completely different.

   Here are a few selections from Luther's writing to illustrate his orientation was not reform but revolution:

"I have cast the die; I now despise the rage of the Romans as much as I do their favor. I will not reconcile myself to them for all eternity, nor have anything to do with them. Let them condemn and burn all that belongs to me. In return, I also will do as much for them; otherwise I could not kindle the fire that is to condemn and burn, before the eyes of the worlds, the whole Papal system" (Letter to his friend Spalatin, 1520).

"If I succeed in doing away with the Mass, then I shall believe I have completely conquered the Pope. If the sacrilegious and cursed custom of the Mass is overthrown, then the whole must fall" (Letter to Henry VIII, 1522).

3. *Martin Luther criticized the authority of the papacy and the issuance of indulgences in his 95 Theses. What is an indulgence? What was the real problem with indulgences at that time?*

An indulgence is "a remission before God of the temporal punishment due to sins whose guilt has already been forgiven, which the faithful Christian who is duly disposed gains under certain prescribed conditions through the action of the Church which, as the minister of redemption, dispenses and applies with authority the treasury of the satisfactions of Christ and the saints. An indulgence is partial or plenary according as it removes either part or all of the temporal punishment due to sin. The faithful can gain indulgences for themselves or apply them to the dead" (*Catechism of the Catholic Church*, 1471).

When we sin we make a free-willed offense against God and our neighbor. Through sacramental confession and an attitude of contrition, the guilt of sin is forgiven by God, but in justice, the hurt caused by our sin needs to be healed. This is the temporal punishment due to sin. For example, if we broke someone's window, we can express true sorrow and ask forgiveness from the person. However, justice demands we also make restitution for the harm we have caused; in this case, we should replace the window. An indulgence means justice is satisfied through certain prescribed actions, like going on a pilgrimage, praying, fasting or even giving alms. Through the treasury of grace administered by the Church we can receive a partial or plenary (i.e., full) remission of the temporal punishment due to our sins.

Indulgences have a long and well-documented history in the Church. The legitimate issue in the sixteenth century was not whether indulgences were allowed (although Luther did raise that point) but whether one could receive an indulgence through almsgiving. Although alms giving also has a long history and tradition in the Church, sixteenth-century preachers did not always provide theologically correct explanations to the faithful and even at times scandalously stated the payment of money would free souls from purgatory. Many people came to believe they could purchase their own salvation or help their deceased relatives enter heaven by giving money to these preachers. This was a serious abuse of a long held doctrine, which, unfortunately, remained unchecked for years.

4. *In 1520, Luther wrote three very important treatises that outlined his revolutionary plan. Name the three treatises. What were Luther's main teachings and how do they contradict Catholic teaching?*

Luther's three major treatises in 1520 were:

1. *Appeal to the Christian Nobility of the German Nation*

2. *On the Babylonian Captivity of the Church*

3. *On Christian Liberty*

In these treatises, Luther expounds on his vision for a new church, separated from Rome and nationally based. He advocates personal interpretation of Scripture, *sola scriptura* ("Scripture alone," the idea that the only authoritative source of divine revelation is the Sacred Scriptures), *sola fides* ("Faith alone," the idea that one is justified solely through faith), the destruction of the entire sacramental system (Luther would maintain two sacraments, baptism and Eucharist, though his theology of the Eucharist differed markedly from Catholic teaching), and a denial of free will.

Luther's main teachings contradict Catholic teaching in important ways. His belief in *sola scriptura* denies the validity of Sacred Tradition (i.e., teachings given by Christ to His apostles and handed down and preserved through the centuries in the Church) as an authoritative source of God's Revelation. His belief that one is saved through faith alone and that good works do not contribute to one's salvation is contrary to the Faith as taught and lived since apostolic times. Luther believed that God did not endow humanity with the gift of free will; we are simply malleable creatures used by God or the devil and their usage of us determines our eternal destiny. In other words, there is nothing we can do to influence whether we spend eternity with God in heaven or with the devil in hell. Luther also advocated the theological position of the total depravity of man. He believed that as a result of original sin, human nature was totally corrupted and depraved of God's grace and life. Because of original sin, a wrathful, vengeful God wants to punish humanity but in His love, He sends His Son as the perfect man to serve as a shield between God and man. God desires to punish humanity, but He sees the perfect love and obedience of His Son and therefore withholds His punishment. He also described humanity as a dunghill that by Christ's saving actions is covered with grace like snow. On the contrary, Catholic teaching articulates a belief in concupiscence, that human nature, as a result of original sin, was not totally corrupted but wounded. Humanity is not deprived of God's grace and life but only deprived of it through sin. The effect of original sin produces the inclination to sin in man (known as concupiscence). Man is tempted to sin but does not have to give in to that temptation, he has a choice to avoid or to give in. Christ came to restore our relationship with God and through His grace we are made new and given the strength to fight concupiscence and live in the state of friendship with God and our neighbor.

5. *What happened at the Diet of Worms?*

After Luther's public burning of the papal bull *Exsurge Domine* ("Arise, O Lord") and his steadfast refusal to recant his heretical teachings, Pope Leo X excommunicated him. The papal legate in Germany, Cardinal Aleander, encouraged the Holy Roman Emperor, a young Charles V and the German Diet (an assembly of nobles) to arrest Luther and try him for heresy. Charles V was devoutly Catholic and desired uniformity of faith in his realm. However, debate raged in the Diet, as several prominent nobles actively supported Luther and his cause against the Church. Ultimately, the Diet demanded Luther be allowed one last opportunity to recant. Charles V accepted this request and sent word to Luther requesting his appearance at Worms under imperial safe conduct.

At the Diet, Johann Eck, who had famously debated Luther at the city of Leipzig in 1519, asked Luther to recant the heretical teachings contained in his books (which were on a table before him). Luther asked for time to consider his answer, and he was given one day. The next day, Luther stood before the assembly and said he would not recant anything he had written unless what he had written was proved wrong through the "testimony of the Scriptures and by evident reasoning." He also stated he would not listen to the pope or the teachings of the Church, only Scripture. Debate raged in the Diet, and Elector Frederick of Saxony, Luther's lord, who had been secretly supportive of Luther before the Diet, openly took Luther's side. Charles V decided the matter by stating, "For it is certain that a single monk must err if he stands against the opinion of all Christendom. Otherwise Christendom itself would have erred for more than a thousand years. From now on I regard him as a notorious heretic…"

Luther was allowed to leave Worms, since he was still under the protection of an imperial safe conduct. On his way home, he was "kidnapped" by Elector Frederick's forces and taken to a safe house where he lived in hiding for the next year spending his time working on his translation of the Old Testament into German.

6. *Rome has been sacked numerous times in its history. The Sack of 1527 is particularly appalling because it came at the hands of imperial troops whose leader held the title, "Protector of the Pope." Why did this sack occur? What were its effects?*

The Sack of Rome in 1527 is a perfect example of the pope involving himself in temporal affairs to the detriment of himself and the Church. Francis I of France and the Holy Roman Emperor Charles V were at odds over the city of Milan. Both men prepared their armies to battle in Italy. Pope Clement VII believed the French were more powerful, so he entered into a secret alliance with Francis I to weaken the power of Charles V in Italy. Charles received news of the pope's betrayal and, after defeating the French forces and capturing Francis I, he kept his army in Italy to pressure Clement. Negotiations between the Holy Roman Emperor and the pope stalled while the imperial army, comprised mostly of German Lutheran mercenaries, grew impatient. The army marched on Rome and broke through the defenses of the city on May 6. Pope Clement VII ran for his life down the covered passageway from the Vatican to Castel Sant' Angelo while the Swiss Guards covered his retreat with their lives (147 were killed that day). The imperial army ransacked the city for over a week killing approximately 12,000 people and committing all forms of heinous and blasphemous crimes. Clement eventually surrendered, and the army left the city.

The sack came at a crucial time in the conflict with Martin Luther. The troubles in Italy leading to the sack prevented both Charles V and Clement VII to focus their attention to the situation in Germany, which allowed it to fester out of control. The sack would also affect England since this was the time when Henry VIII asked Clement for an annulment from Catherine of Aragon, who was Charles V's aunt! Clement was in position to grant the annulment (if one should have been granted) given his precarious relationship with Charles.

7. *Cardinal Cajetan met with Martin Luther and tried to avert a crisis and bring Luther back into the fold; he failed. What would you have said to Luther?*

Answers will vary but a few things to consider. Cardinal Cajetan tried to reason with Luther using Thomistic arguments. Luther despised Aquinas and the whole scholastic method. Thus, he was not disposed to listen to Cardinal Cajetan, no matter how rational or logical the argument. This helps to illustrate an important point when defending the faith: know your audience. It is highly desirable to get background on the individual before discussing the Faith. This is easily accomplished given enough time, but even in spur of the moment conversations with strangers, asking some personal questions to help you understand the person's background and interests can do this. Knowing a little bit about the person makes it easier to formulate meaningful responses to their questions. Of course, you may not convince the person of the veracity of the Faith but hopefully, you can help them understand the Church's teaching, even if they disagree with it and if you are able to make a personal connection through your questioning then perhaps the Lord will provide another opportunity for you to take the conversation deeper.

D. Application

Discussion Leaders: If time permits, ask the group members to share their personal responses to the application question.

Martin Luther was a very complicated and conflicted man. He shared his personal beliefs with others in order to influence them to leave the Faith. His personal disagreement with certain teachings of the Church became public, which destroyed the unity of the Church and European society. One person's Faith (or lack thereof) can have huge ramifications for others. How do you influence others about the Catholic Church? Who has influenced you the most in your faith life? What can you do to ensure you provide a positive influence to others about the Catholic Faith?

Close with the prayer found in the Leader's Guide.

Protestors & Defenders – Part II

A. Review the Context

Discussion Leaders: Make sure everyone has their *Epic* Church History Timeline chart to use when discussing questions about the time period. Briefly go over the other sections of the chart especially the Events & Influences section so that you can situate the story of the Church in the larger story of the world.

B. Learn the Story

Discussion Leaders: Unless there are comments or questions about Steve Weidenkopf's presentation, dive into answering the discussion questions in Section C.

C. Take a Deeper Look

1. *Hilaire Belloc described John Calvin as the one "who began the war against Joy." Who was John Calvin? Why did Belloc describe him that way?*

    John Calvin was a French layman who accepted Protestant teachings in 1533 and then moved to the town of Basel (in modern-day Switzerland). Calvin wrote his *Institutes of the Christian Religion* in 1536, which served as the articulation of his main heretical beliefs. Calvin moved to Geneva and established the first Christian theocracy where the civil and church government were one. He passed ordinances, which regulated the personal lives of the citizens in keeping with his teachings. Belloc playfully describes Calvin as the one "who began the war against joy" because of the harsh and repressive measures instituted in Geneva under Calvin. He outlawed dancing, singing, jewelry, using makeup, staging or attending theatrical plays and naming children after anyone but Old Testament figures. Capital crimes included adultery, pregnancy out of wedlock, blasphemy, heresy, idolatry, and striking a parent. Christians were required to confess their sins to a magistrate in a court of law. In light of these restrictions, it is easy to understand why Belloc believed a war against joy was the centerpiece of Calvin's rule in Geneva.

2. *What is the importance of Calvin and his teachings?*

    Calvin is a very important figure in the Protestant revolution. He was the organizer of the movement because he produced a church, a creed, and a discipline. He established a hierarchically-organized church in Geneva, wrote a creed (the *Institutes*), and developed a way of life. Although Luther railed against the Church and her teachings, and even advocated a separate church, he did not produce an organized, unified institution. Calvin did. Calvin's writings were spread throughout Europe and influenced such figures as John Knox in Scotland and Thomas Cranmer in England. Calvin wrote numerous letters to Protestant leaders throughout Europe encouraging them in their rebellion. He established a university to ensure his teachings were studied and developed. Finally, because he ruled the city of Geneva he gave the world an example of how the Protestant system worked. This was very different from Germany, where Luther was not a political ruler and where violence and warfare erupted. Calvin organized and systemized Protestant thought ensuring it would continue and develop in the following centuries.

3. *Evangelization efforts in Mexico before 1532, although vigorous, only produced 200,000 baptisms. In a four-year period from 1532–1536, 1.3 million people were baptized. What happened to affect such a significant change?*

On December 12, 1531 a miracle occurred that changed the history of the Mexican people. Ten years earlier, the Spanish explorer Hernan Cortes conquered the Aztec empire. The Aztecs were a fierce people who practiced ritual human sacrifice. It is estimated approximately 50,000 people were sacrificed each year to satisfy the satanic hunger of the Aztec gods. Cortes brought the light of the Gospel into this darkness, but the conversion of the populace was a tiresome venture that did not produce significant results. But that would change after the appearance of the Lady. The Blessed Mother appeared to St. Juan Diego and asked him to go to the bishop and ask that a shrine may be built in her honor on Tepeyac hill. Juan Diego went to the bishop and told him about Our Lady's appearance to him and what she had requested. The bishop demanded proof before he would act. A few days later Our Lady appeared again to Juan Diego. She told him to pick roses from Tepeyac hill and deliver them to the bishop. St. Juan did as instructed, and when he released his tilma, the roses fell to the floor revealing a miraculous image of Our Lady. After the appearance of the Blessed Mother, the fruits of evangelization efforts in Mexico produced significant accomplishments as more than a million people were baptized. The Faith that would be sorely tested in the twentieth century was made permanent in Mexico through a Mother's love.

4. *The Faith in England was lost over the desires of one man. What happened in England during this time period?*

The Tudor family ascended the throne in England through violence by winning the Battle of Bosworth Field in 1485, and violence against the Faith and the faithful would be their lasting legacy. Henry VIII succeeded his father as king in 1509. He was happily married to Catherine of Aragon, daughter of Fernando and Isabel of Spain, who bore him a daughter, Mary. Over time, the temptations of court life were too much for Henry and he took mistresses. One in particular, Anne Boleyn, controlled Henry and demanded he divorce Catherine and marry her. Henry commissioned the archbishop of Canterbury, Cardinal Wolsely, to procure an annulment from the pope. Pope Clement VII was in a precarious position due to the presence of imperial troops in Rome commanded by Catherine's nephew Charles V, so he refused to make a quick decision. He did allow a tribunal to meet in England to gather testimony and evidence. The tribunal met, and both Henry and Catherine testified. The bishops were asked to support the king's cause, and all but one, St. John Fisher, did. Clement, however, received an impassioned letter from Catherine and remanded the case to Rome. This caused the downfall of Cardinal Wolsely, who was forced to resign as lord chancellor (to be replaced by St. Thomas More). Henry still wanted the annulment, and his prime minister provided the way to receive it. Thomas Cromwell suggested Henry make himself the head of the Church in England, so that his bishops could do his bidding and not the pope's. Henry embraced the suggestion and, after the death of Wolsely, appointed Thomas Cranmer, a secret Lutheran, as archbishop of Canterbury. Cranmer declared Henry and Catherine's marriage invalid, and then presided over the "marriage" of Anne and Henry.

In March 1534, Pope Clement VII gave his official answer to Henry—his annulment was denied. Henry then called on the English parliament to pass two pieces of legislation that separated England from the Catholic Church. The first was the Act of Succession, which declared Henry' marriage to Catherine invalid, his marriage to Anne valid, and Elizabeth (his child with Anne) as the legitimate heir to the throne. Next came the Act of Supremacy, which declared the king to be the supreme head of the Church in England. Both acts required oaths, refusal of which was considered treason.

Henry brought the Church in England into schism by refusing to acknowledge the pope as the head of the Church on Earth. Unfortunately, England would enter into heresy after Henry's death through the efforts of Thomas Cranmer and Edward VI (Henry's son from Jane Seymour).

5. *Many courageous saints refused to enter into schism when ordered by their government to reject the authority of the pope. Who were some of these saints? What are their stories?*

Although many brave men and women would give their lives for the Faith in England during Henry's reign, and particularly in the reign of Elizabeth, his daughter, two martyrs during this time stand out: Sts. John Fisher and Thomas More.

St. John Fisher (1449–1535) was the bishop of Rochester and lived a very austere, penitential and holy life. During the marriage tribunal he was the only bishop (out of 300) to defend the validity of Catherine and Henry's marriage. He refused to take the Oath of Succession and was arrested and imprisoned in the Tower of London. Pope Paul III created him a cardinal in the hopes that Henry would not dare execute a cardinal. Henry had no qualms and had St. John Fisher tried and convicted. He was executed at Tyburn by beheading on June 22, 1535. His head was mounted on a spike on London Bridge for two weeks and then thrown into the Thames to serve as a warning to others who might endeavor to maintain the authentic faith.

St. Thomas More (1478–1535) was a lawyer and judge by profession as well as a loving husband and father by vocation. Henry appointed him Lord Chancellor of England after removing Cardinal Wolsely. After the event known as the Submission of the Clergy, where Henry, in essence, demanded their complete submission to his whims, St. Thomas More resigned as Chancellor. He too refused to take Oath of Succession and was imprisoned for fifteen months in the Tower. Tried and convicted of treason he was executed on July 6, 1535. At his execution he tied his own blindfold and told the crowd that he would die "in the faith and for the faith of the Catholic Church, being the King's good servant, but God's first."

Both men and others not as well known serve as reminders for us that our faith in Christ and His Church must be on firm foundation in order to withstand and temptation or threats to repudiate it. Their witness is a heroic one in our day and age that is in serious need of the good example of those who reject worldly enticements for the grandeur of eternal life.

D. Application

Discussion Leaders: If time permits, ask the group members to share their personal responses to the application question.

In his gospel, St. John records the prayer of Jesus for his followers: "That they may all be one; even as thou, Father, art in me, and I in thee, that they also may be in us, so that the world may believe that thou hast sent me" (John 17:21). This time period illustrates the fact that Christians have failed to live that prayer of Christ fully. Indeed, the last five hundred years of the Faith has been marked by the complete disintegration of unity among Western Christians. There are over 33,000 different groupings of Christians in the world whereas before 1517 there were only two major groups (Byzantines and Latins). What can we do to restore unity to the Church, as Jesus desired? How have I presented the Faith and the Church to my Protestant family members, friends, co-workers? Do I pray for the restoration of Christian unity?

Close with the prayer found in the Leader's Guide.

E. Wrap-up

1. *What is the color of this time period? How can you remember it?*

    Remember the Protestors & Defenders time period by its color, orange: it is a traditional Protestant color and is associated with William of Orange who led the successful revolt against King James II in 1688 ensuring England remained a Protestant nation.

2. *What is the main theme of this period?*

    The main theme of the Protestors & Defenders period is the breaking of Christendom and revolution against the Church through the actions of Martin Luther, John Calvin, and Henry VIII.

3. *Write a one- or two-sentence summary of the Protestors & Defenders period in order to recall the main events of Church history during this time.*

    Answers will vary but they should contain most of the main events listed on the *Epic* Church History Timeline chart.

The Catholic Reformation – Part I

A. Review the Context

Discussion Leaders: Make sure everyone has their *Epic* Church History Timeline chart to use when discussing questions about the time period. Briefly go over the other sections of the chart especially the Events & Influences section so that you can situate the story of the Church in the larger story of the world.

B. Learn the Story

Discussion Leaders: Unless there are comments or questions about Steve Weidenkopf's presentation, dive into answering the discussion questions in Section C.

C. Take a Deeper Look

1. *Archbishop Cranmer succeeded in moving England from schism to heresy. How did he accomplish this?*

   After the death of Henry VIII in 1547, Archbishop Cranmer moved England into heresy through a series of changes to the liturgy and the ritual for ordaining priests. The young Edward VI and Parliament provided Cranmer with the royal and legal backing he needed to separate England from the Catholic Faith.

   Cranmer devised a new liturgy, which was outlined in two editions of the *Book of Common Prayer*. This new liturgy removed all references to the Mass as a sacrifice and renamed the sacrament "The Lord's Supper." Eucharistic processions and adorations were outlawed. All English subjects were required to attend approved Anglican services every Sunday and strictly forbidden under pain of imprisonment from attending a Catholic Mass.

   The move to heresy was complete with the revision to the Ordinal, the ritual used to ordain bishops and priests. Cranmer's revision once again attacked the Eucharistic nature of the priesthood by denying the priest acted *in persona Christi* to re-present Christ's salvific sacrifice. This denial of the sacrificial nature of the priesthood is in essence a denial of the very nature of the priesthood and as such produces a break in apostolic succession nullifying Holy Orders. Pope Leo XIII explicitly stated this Ordinal broke the line of apostolic succession and created invalid Holy Orders in his 1896 pronouncement, *Apostolicae Curiae*.

2. *Mary Tudor is often referred, as "Bloody Mary" while her half-sister Elizabeth is known as "Good Queen Bess." Are these labels accurate? Why or Why not?*

   Mary Tudor lived a very difficult life. She witnessed the very public and nasty divorce of her parents. She was declared illegitimate and unable to rule by a decree of Parliament. Her father clearly favored her half-sister and forbade her even to see her mother. Throughout these difficulties, Mary maintained her faith in God and His Church. When she ascended the throne after the death of her half-brother, Edward, and the short reign of Lady Jane Grey, Mary was convinced that her deliverance was part of God's plan to restore the Faith to England. She undertook this divine mandate with enthusiasm and strength of mind and will. Mary's reign was not entirely secure, as rebels organized who disliked Mary for her politics as well as her restoration of Catholicism. For both political and religious reasons, they endeavored to overthrow her. Rebels who were captured were tried as heretics and executed at the stake. In the last two years of her short reign, 273 persons were executed for threatening her reign.

These numbers sharply contrast with the more than 700 documented cases of priests and laity executed for the Faith under Elizabeth. Elizabeth undertook the largest state-sponsored persecution of Catholics since the Roman Empire. Priests were hunted and laity who harbored them were arrested, imprisoned and persecuted.

History in the United States has been traditionally written with an English Protestant worldview. Therefore, Mary Tudor was—and still is—labeled "Bloody Mary," and portrayed as the persecutor of reform-minded English Protestants. Elizabeth, on the other hand, has consistently (especially in several recent high-profile Hollywood films) been portrayed as a good queen who made England into a world power. Rarely is her policy of state-sponsored persecution of Catholics ever mentioned.

3.   *Who were some of the English martyrs of this period?*

Although there were many martyrs in England throughout this period, two martyrs should be mentioned, St. Edmund Campion (1540–1581) and St. Margaret Clitherow (1556–1586).

St. Edmund Campion was a Jesuit who left England to study for the priesthood in order to be sent back to his home country to minister to the underground Catholics. After his ordination, St. Edmund returned to England in 1580 and began his clandestine work among the persecuted faithful. St. Edmund's work was not entirely secret as he published a book known as "Campion's Brag," in which he defended the Faith and exhorted his fellow countrymen to return to the Church. The Elizabethan government had issued a law charging any citizen with abiding and abetting rebellion if they failed to turn a Jesuit over to the state. It was also a capital offense to convert an Englishmen to the Catholic Faith. St. Edmund was eventually betrayed and turned over to the authorities. He was brutally tortured on the rack and with the tearing off of his fingernails. He was tried for treason. Despite his wounds, he defended himself with competence—though the jury was bribed in order to ensure conviction. When the guilty sentence was read, St. Edmund responded, "In condemning us, you condemn all your own ancestors—all the ancient priests, bishops, and kings—all that was once the glory of England, the island of saints, and the most devoted child of the See of Peter. For what have we taught, however, you may qualify it with the odious name of treason that they did not uniformly teach? To be condemned with these old lights—not of England only, but of the world, by their degenerate descendants, is both gladness and glory to us." He was executed by hanging, drawing, and quartering on December 1, 1581.

St. Margaret Clitherow was a joy-filled, loving wife and mother who converted to the Catholic faith in 1574. Her husband remained Protestant, but she instructed her children in the outlawed faith. She assisted and hid priests and was arrested and imprisoned several times. Many of her priests were martyred and she made secret pilgrimages to Tyburn (the place of martyrdom) to pray. In 1586, she was arrested and tried for treason. She refused to plead for fear of incriminating the only witnesses to her activities, her children and servants. She was sentenced to death by being pressed by a huge rock. Despite her pregnancy, the sentence was carried out on Good Friday. Her children maintained the Faith and responded to God's call by becoming priests and entering religious life.

4.   *An agreement was reached in Germany in 1555 ending the Catholic–Protestant conflict. What was the name of that agreement? What were the details? Did it bring about lasting peace?*

The Peace of Augsburg ended the bloody nine-year Catholic–Protestant conflict that erupted in Germany in the middle of the sixteenth century. The terms of the peace were favorable to the Lutherans, as their territories were given legal recognition and equal sovereignty with Catholic states. Lutherans were allowed total religious autonomy in their areas and were able to keep any Church property seized during the conflict. The main element of the peace was the procedure used to determine the religion of a region. The determining factor hinged on the ruler of the state. If he was Catholic then everyone in his realm was Catholic. This policy was known as *cuius regio, eius religio* ("Whose rule, his religion"). Those who held to the opposite faith of the ruler were allowed to sell their property and leave. Ultimately, no one was happy with the terms of the peace and it sowed the seeds of discord in Germany leading later to the brutal and bloody Thirty Years War (1618–1648).

5. *The Council of Trent is one of the most significant events in Church history. What happened at this council? What were some of its teachings?*

Pope Paul III (1534–1549) initially convoked the Council of Trent in 1545 in response to the Protestant crises. The main purpose of the council was to define authentic Catholic doctrine and reform the life of the Church. Trent met over an eighteen-year period in intermittent sessions, which were suspended twice due to illness and war. Expectations were high, as Catholic critics of the numerous ecclesiastical abuses desired reform. Additionally, the Church had not issued any formal doctrinal statements in response to the Lutheran rebellion in Germany since Pope Leo X's *Exsurge Domine* in 1520.

The Council of Trent undertook an extensive doctrinal review of all the sacraments, providing definitive statements on each one. They also reaffirmed several Catholic teachings attacked by Luther and Calvin—namely, that the deposit of faith is comprised of both Sacred Scripture and Sacred Tradition; the Sacred Scriptures are comprised of seventy-three books (forty-six Old Testament and twenty-seven New Testament); Christ instituted the hierarchical structure of the Church (i.e., bishops, priests, laity); man is not depraved as a result of original sin but rather deprived of God's grace; man suffers from a wounded not corrupted nature that is tempted to sin (this teaching is known as concupiscence); and faith alone (*sola fides*) is not sufficient for justification but rather man is saved by faith in Christ, accompanied by participation in the other theological virtues of hope and love and illustrated through the performance of good works.

The bishops acknowledged their failings and faults as contributing to the divided situation of Christendom and expressed true repentance for their sins. This expression was backed by the passing of several reform decrees aimed at purifying and strengthening the clergy, so that they might give an authentic and efficacious witness of faith to the laity. One important reform decree was the requirement for bishops to establish a seminary in their diocese in order to properly instruct and form priests. In addition, Trent called for the revision of the Roman Missal and the promulgation of a universal catechism for use in instructing the faithful.

6. *The Catholic Reformation emphasized three "D's." What were they and how were they implemented?*

The three "D's" of the Catholic Reformation were doctrine, discipline, and devotion. An authentic reformation must address all three elements.

The Council of Trent addressed all three elements through a reiteration of Catholic doctrinal beliefs, the reform of Church life through decrees against the numerous ecclesiastical abuses, and by calling for the reform of the liturgy in order to foster a more unified and pious worship. Pope St. Pius V enforced the discipline decrees of Trent and promulgated a universal catechism (doctrine) and revised the celebration of the liturgy (devotion).

D. Application

Discussion Leaders: If time permits, ask the group members to share their personal responses to the application question.

The Church was in serious need of reform. That reform came about through the Council of Trent and the actions of Pope St. Pius V, the Jesuits and many holy men and women. In some ways, the Church is always in need of purification and reform, especially concerning the lives of her members. What areas of your life are in need of reform? In what ways can we make reparation for the sins of members of the Church? Why is this important?

Close with the prayer found in the Leader's Guide.

The Catholic Reformation – Part II

A. Review the Context

Discussion Leaders: Make sure everyone has their *Epic* Church History Timeline chart to use when discussing questions about the time period. Briefly go over the other sections of the chart especially the Events & Influences section so that you can situate the story of the Church in the larger story of the world.

B. Learn the Story

Discussion Leaders: Unless there are comments or questions about Steve Weidenkopf's presentation, dive into answering the discussion questions in Section C.

C. Take a Deeper Look

1. *The decrees of a council need to be implemented for there to be any lasting change in the Church. Who implemented the decrees of Trent? How?*

   Pope St. Pius V (1566–1572), the father of the Catholic Reformation, successfully implemented the decrees of Trent. He promulgated a universal catechism in 1566 (it would remain the only universal catechism in the Church for 426 years until the *Catechism of the Catholic Church* promulgated by Pope John Paul II in 1992) and reformed the Roman Missal in 1570, mandating its use throughout the Latin Church. These reforms helped to reunify the Church and, in terms of the catechism, provided an authentic and published response to Protestant attacks on Catholic doctrine.

   Pius V was assisted in implementing the decrees of Trent by his trusted "shock troops," the Jesuits. St. Ignatius and his brave band of compatriots were sent throughout the old to spread the Faith and combat heresy. They created a successful educational system through the establishment of colleges and universities throughout Christendom. Their tireless efforts on behalf of the pope and the Church ensured the success of the Catholic Reformation.

   The Church was in serious need of reform, and the Protestant crisis demanded a response. The Council of Trent satisfied both requirements and provided the Church with a firm foundation to withstand the turbulent centuries ahead.

2. *The Battle of Lepanto is one of the most significant events in the history of the Church. Why? What happened?*

   Throughout the sixteenth century Muslim forces had invaded central Europe and raided throughout the Mediterranean Sea. Christendom was on the defense and the Turks were planning a large campaign against Rome. The very existence of Christendom and the heart of the Church were threatened. Pope St. Pius V attempted to form a large Christian force to check the Muslim advance, but most major European nations were not interested. The English under Elizabeth were not remotely interested in helping the pope. The French were concerned only with their own national interests and had even entered into alliances with the Turks. Only Spain and the Italian city-state of Venice joined the papal forces to form the Holy League. Don Juan of Austria, the twenty-four-year-old illegitimate son of the

Holy Roman Emperor Charles V and half-brother of the King of Spain, Philip II, was chosen to lead the largest Christian fleet ever assembled.

Don Juan engaged a superior Muslim fleet in the Gulf of Lepanto on October 7, 1571. Through skillful tactics and a miraculous change in the wind, the Christian fleet won an overwhelming victory. The Muslim fleet was utterly destroyed. As a result, the Turks would never again mount a serious offensive from the sea. Rome and Christendom were saved.

3. *This time period is witness to several saints who contributed to the reform of the Church. Name several and discuss their role in the Catholic Reformation.*

The saints who helped reform the Church during this period can be organized into two groups, mystics and activists. The mystics were St. Teresa of Avila (1515–1582) and St. John of the Cross (1542–1591). Both reformed the Carmelite order and wrote beloved mystical classics that are still read today. The reform of the Carmelite order provided a necessary level of sanctification in the Church and greatly contributed to the Catholic Reformation.

The activist saints who, through a holy and tireless witness, actively pursued the reform of the Church were St. Charles Borromeo (1538–1584), St. Philip Neri (1515–1595) and St. Francis de Sales (1567–1622). St. Charles Borromeo embarked on the reform of his archdiocese of Milan, a place that had not seen a resident archbishop (because of the abuse of absenteeism) in 100 years. St. Charles vowed to make himself the living symbol of the Catholic Reformation. He established a seminary in Milan and exhorted his priests to live holy lives. Called home to the Lord at the early age of forty-six, he was one of the lights of the authentic reformation. St. Philip Neri was called to provide a holy witness in the Eternal City where he reformed souls through his personal example. He lived a simple, holy life, visited the catacombs for prayer, led pilgrimages to the churches of Rome, visited hospitals, preached and exhorted people to serve God, and spent long periods in the confessional. He also helped to reform priestly life through the establishment of the Congregation of the Oratory (Oratorians) where diocesan priests would live in community without vows in order to strengthen one another in holiness. St. Francis de Sales special calling was to the land of Calvin. Named bishop of Geneva in 1602, St. Francis was a tireless worker for the conversion of Protestants. He was a master apologist for the faith and the author of the still-read spiritual classic *Introduction to the Devout Life.*

4. *Critics often accuse the Church of remaining silent and even advocating the slavery of indigenous people. Are these accusations accurate? How would you respond to someone who advocated these criticisms?*

Spain was able to launch a massive colonization effort in the New World because of the efforts of her great monarchs, Fernando and Isabel. They set the stage for future colonization and evangelization efforts through their support of Columbus and their work to unite Spain and preserve it from the religious wars then tearing Europe apart. Unfortunately, in Mexico and South and Central America, the heinous practice of slavery crept into the Spanish colonies. Due to a shortage of manpower, the Spanish originally utilized Indians for labor (in which they did receive wages in some cases), but this act of service soon gave way to outright slavery. Pope Paul III issued a severe condemnation of slavery in 1537 when he wrote, "We, by Our apostolic authority, do hereby determine and declare, that notwithstanding, what may have been said in the p*ast or what may be said in the future, the… Indians… are by no means to be deprived of their liberty … they are not to be reduced to slavery.*" Many missionaries, including Bartholomew de las Casas (1474–1566), spoke out against slavery and in favor of the rights of the Indians. A hundred years later, the situation had changed in South America where thousands of African slaves were brought over to work in the colonies. One estimate indicates the Portuguese brought 3,000 to 5,000 African slaves a year to Columbia. Once again, the pope (Urban VIII) issued a decree forbidding the capture and removal of Africans from their native country. St. Peter Claver (1581–1654) arrived in Columbia and ministered to the African slaves, even at the docks as the slave ships arrived. St. Peter's work among the African slaves produced great fruit as he baptized more than 300,000 Africans over the course of his ministry. He was a holy man who cared deeply for the slaves and imitated Christ through his charity. Pope Leo XIII remarked, "No life, except the life of Christ, has so moved me as that of St. Peter Claver."

5. *The French were very active in missionary work in North America during this time period. Who were some of the holy men and women who carried the Gospel to the New World?*

The French began their exploration of North America with the arrival of Jacques Cartier who explored the area around the St. Lawrence Seaway in the middle sixteenth century. Half a century later, Samuel de Champlain established Quebec City. Missionaries were sent to New France to minister to the French colonists as well as to evangelize the native Indian population. One such missionary was Marie Guyart (Bl. Marie de l'Incarnatione; 1599–1672). After the death of her husband, Marie entered an Ursuline convent. St. Angela de Merici founded the Ursulines in 1535 to teach women, help orphaned girls, and prevent women from entering prostitution. Marie took this apostolate of the order to Quebec City where she founded a girls-only school (still in operation today). She focused much attention on educating the Indians, and, after learning the Iroquois, Algonquian, and Huron languages, she prepared catechisms for the Indians to help them learn the Faith.

New France also witnessed the arrival of many Jesuits, several of whom became martyrs. Included in this august group are St. Isaac Jogues (1607–1646) and St. John de Brébeuf (1593–1649). Both worked among the Hurons and were captured by members of the fierce and savage nations of the Iroquois Confederacy (the Oneidas, Onondagas, Senecas, Mohawks, and Cayugas). St. Isaac suffered for a year in captivity and was brutally tortured, losing several fingers in the process. He escaped captivity and made his way back home to France. After a short while, though, he petitioned to return to New France, and he was martyred along with companions in 1646. St. Jean established good relations with the Hurons, learning their language and writing a catechism and dictionary. Captured by the Iroquois, he was brutally tortured to death. Their martyrdom produced conversions including the most famous Native American Christian, Bl. Kateri Tekawitha (1656–1680), who was born ten years after the death of St. Isaac Jogues in the same village!

6. *What was the real issue between the Church and Galileo?*

The sixteenth and seventeenth centuries were witness to dramatic advances in mathematics, physics, chemistry, physiology, geometry, and astronomy. Many of these advances were the result of the Church's influence. For example, Pope Gregory XIII reformed the calendar in 1578 through the efforts of the brilliant Jesuit scientist Christopher Clavius. The world was changing, moving from the "age of faith" to the "age of reason." One dramatic advance shaped a young professor of mathematics at the University of Padua named Galileo—namely, Copernicus' theory that the earth revolved around the sun. Galileo was fascinated with this theory and set out to prove its truth. While pursuing this noteworthy scientific goal, however, Galileo advocated something much more than the revolution of the earth around the sun. He advanced the notion that science is superior to and even supplants faith in explaining reality. Galileo sought physical answers to metaphysical questions (e.g., What is truth? Why are we here? What is the meaning of life?). In essence, he did not believe in the compatibility of faith and science. This was the real issue between the Church and Galileo, and it remains one of the major issues facing the Church in the modern world.

7. *Many people cite the Galileo affair as evidence the Church is against science. Is this an accurate viewpoint? What is the relationship between faith and reason?*

The "Galileo myth" paints a picture of the Catholic Church as a monolithic institution bent on maintaining control over Europe while suppressing authentic scientific research and silencing scientists such as Galileo.This myth has absolutely no bearing in historical reality. The Church's response to Galileo was guided by a concern for the maintenance of a worldview that acknowledged the role of both faith and reason in explaining reality. Although the judgment against Galileo was not pastorally prudent, it was not an attempt by the Church to squash scientific research. There is a complementary relationship between faith and reason; both are needed to understand life and the world. By using both faculties, humanity can come to know more about God and the world He created. The details of the confrontation between Galileo and the Church are complex, and historical truth is not served through the perpetuation of myths or the use of polemics. It is an issue that still affects the Church today and how people view her so Catholics have a special duty to study and learn more about this dramatic episode in the history of the Church.

D. Application

Discussion Leaders: If time permits, ask the group members to share their personal responses to the application question.

Galileo attempted to answer metaphysical questions (e.g. What is truth? What is reality?) with physical answers. Galileo believed and advocated that science is superior to and supplants faith. His underlying premise was there is only one path to explaining the truth of reality - observation and reason – all other explanations are wrong. The Church countered Galileo with insisting on the complimentary of faith and reason. Both help to explain the world God created because both come from God. Pope John Paul II beautifully expressed the Church's teaching in this area in the introduction to his encyclical Fides et Ratio: *"Faith and reason are like two wings on which the human spirit rises to the contemplation of truth; and God has placed in the human heart a desire to know the truth—in a word, to know himself—so that, by knowing and loving God, men and women may also come to the fullness of truth about themselves." Do you desire to know the truth? How do you go about that? How can we know the fullness of ourselves by knowing God? How do I see the relationship between faith and reason?*

Close with the prayer found in the Leader's Guide.

E. Wrap-up

1. *What is the color of this time period? How can you remember it?*

Remember The Catholic Reformation time period by its color, gold for the many holy men and women God called to help reform the Church.

2. *What is the main theme of this period?*

The main theme of The Catholic Reformation period is the reform of the Church accomplished through the Council of Trent as implemented by Pope St. Pius V and the actions of the Jesuits and other holy saints.

3. *Write a one- or two-sentence summary of The Catholic Reformation period in order to recall the main events of Church history during this time.*

Answers will vary but they should contain most of the main events listed on the *Epic* Church History Timeline chart.

Revolutions & Modernism

A. Review the Context

Discussion Leaders: Make sure everyone has their *Epic* Church History Timeline chart to use when discussing questions about the time period. Briefly go over the other sections of the chart especially the Events & Influences section so that you can situate the story of the Church in the larger story of the world.

B. Learn the Story

Discussion Leaders: Unless there are comments or questions about Steve Weidenkopf's presentation, dive into answering the discussion questions in Section C.

C. Take a Deeper Look

1. *How did the Enlightenment change philosophy? What was René Descartes' solution to the problem of doubt?*

   The philosophers of the Enlightenment (or the "age of reason") rejected a God-centered society in favor of a man-centered society. They rejected the reasoning of scholastic philosophers such as St. Thomas Aquinas and yearned to make philosophy conform to other mathematical sciences. In doing so, they actually divorced philosophy from reality by claiming that one could not reliably access reality through the five physical senses. In their obsession with trying to understand how someone could "know" something they began to doubt that anyone can "know" anything.

   René Descartes' (1596–1650) attempt at a solution to this impenetrable doubt was his famous maxim, "I think therefore I am." He claimed that, since all things must be doubted, doubt was the only certainty. Doubt, therefore, is the gateway to reality. In actuality, this was more of an intellectual "sleight-of-hand," since one exists even before one can doubt, but it became the foundation for much of modern philosophy.

2. *What motivated the suppression of the Jesuits? How was it achieved?*

   Two forces played a key role in the suppression of the Jesuits. First, the *philosophes*, represented by Voltaire, wanted to destroy the Church because they thought her "superstitions" and illogical doctrines stood in the way of the triumph of reason. They knew that their only hope of defeating the Church was the removal of the Jesuits, who were in charge of Catholic education throughout Europe. The other main force was the Catholic European monarchs, who saw the Jesuits, loyal servants of the pope, as the last obstacle standing in the way of their seizing unrestricted central power.

   The suppression was achieved through the power of the kings. The Jesuits were first expelled in Portugal in 1755, then King Louis XV expelled them from France in 1764, and finally, King Charles III of Spain, relying on his anti-Jesuit chief ministers expelled the order from their own homeland in 1767. Eventually, Pope Clement XIV, who was indebted to King Charles III, signed an order in 1773 to suppress the Jesuits completely. Pope Pius VII restored the order forty-one years later in 1814.

3. *The French Revolution is one of the most awful events in modern history, but countless modern myths have obscured this reality. What were your thoughts on the French Revolution before you started this session of the Epic timeline? Has your opinion changed? What new facts did you learn that surprised you the most?*

Answers may vary depending upon each person's knowledge of the French Revolution. What follows is a short list of ideas that might foster discussion:

- The French Revolution was not a rebellion against a cruel, tyrannical king by the oppressed lower class. King Louis was a benevolent ruler who reduced wasteful government spending, lowered the price of bread, worked to rehabilitate the courts, and abolished the torture of accused prisoners. In addition, he was so concerned with the welfare of his people that, despite being in a financial crisis due to aiding the United States against Britain, he refused to raise taxes. He called the National Assembly to handle the crisis, but the Assembly instead became the breeding ground of the Revolution.

- Marie Antoinette was not a spoiled, rich queen who cared so little for the peasants that, when told that the people had no bread replied, "then let them eat cake" (she never uttered that phrase). Rather, she was a devout Catholic who took her duties seriously and cared deeply for her people. The quote either originates from Rousseau's *Confessions*, written in 1766 (when Marie was only ten years old), or might be attributed to the wife of Louis XIV, about a hundred years before Marie would take the throne. Sheer propaganda linked the quote to Marie Antoinette.

- The Revolution was not simply an attempt to establish liberty through a democratic government; it was actually concerned with completely divorcing the Catholic Faith from the state. Priests and bishops were forced to swear an Oath to the Republic, the Gregorian Calendar was rejected in favor of a "calendar of reason," cathedrals were defaced, relics were destroyed, and eventually religious and laity alike were executed for being "fanatics" for the Faith.

- The Revolution committed countless atrocities against the people, far worse than any French king had ever done. By the end of the Reign of Terror, 20,000 citizens had been beheaded, and among them were many of the original leaders of the Revolution itself, such as Danton and Robespierre.

- Many of the poor peasants of France did not embrace the Revolution. In fact, in the region of the Vendée, poor French farmers rose up to defend the Church and the King and led a ragtag army against the Republic soldiers.

4. *What is Modernism? Can you name some of its principle characteristics?*

Modernism is "the synthesis of all heresies," according to Pope St. Pius X. It was a new attack on the fundamentals of the Faith. Modernism is different from other heresies in that it attacks the Faith from within, not by seeking to change the terminology of the Faith but rather the meaning of those words. For example, a modernist doesn't deny the fact Jesus fed 5,000; rather, he re-interprets the event as one of communal sharing urged by Jesus rather than as a true miracle.

Modernism is rooted in rationalism and completely rejects the existence of the supernatural. It is atheistic in nature, denies the possibility of divine revelation and objective truth by relegating all truth to that which can be experienced, and has a great contempt for virtue and beauty. Since man is viewed as the ultimate creature in the universe, modernism inevitably leads to self-worship, a rejection of self-restraint, an embracing of moral relativism, and even the loss of authentic reason.

5. *Who were some of the great popes that reigned during this time period? What were some of their achievements?*

Pope Bl. Pius IX wrote the encyclical *Qui Pluribus,* in which he taught that faith is not opposed to reason. He also proclaimed the dogma of the Immaculate Conception in 1854, condemned the mistakes of modern philosophy in his *Syllabus of Errors,* convened the First Vatican Council in 1869, and consecrated Christendom to the Sacred Heart of Jesus in 1875.

Pope Bl. Leo XIII was another great pope during this time. He battled Otto von Bismarck during the *Kulturkampf* in Germany, established Church relations with democratic governments, opened the Vatican archives to all scholars, upheld the right of personal property as well as defended the right to a living wage in 1891 in his encyclical *Rerum Novarum,* reinvigorated the study of St. Thomas Aquinas, and wrote the St. Michael Prayer as a weapon in the hands of the faithful engaged in daily spiritual combat.

The last pope of this period, Pope St. Pius X, encouraged frequent reception of the Eucharist, allowed children at the age of reason to make their first communion, reformed sacred music, founded the Pontifical Biblical Institute, and even personally taught children's Sunday catechetical classes. He was known for his great holiness, and one of his most notable achievements was his strong stance against modernism. He condemned modernism in his 1907 encyclical *Pascendi Dominici Gregis,* created a new syllabus that outlined the errors of the modernists, and made all clergy and theology teachers swear an oath against modernism.

6. *What were some of the issues the First Vatican Council was supposed to address? What major documents did it issue? Why was it cut short?*

The First Vatican Council was called to condemn the threat of modernism and rationalistic philosophy, restate the Faith in areas in which it had been attacked, provide safeguards for Christian education and marriage, review clerical life, and issue a doctrinal statement on the Church, in particular examining the relationship between the Church and the new modern democratic states.

The council issued two major documents: *Dei Filius,* which reexamined the relationship between the Church, the Faith, revelation, and reason; and *Pastor Aeternus,* which defined the role of the pope in the Church and his special charism of infallibility. It stated the conditions that must be present for the pope to teach infallibly:

1. He must teach as successor of St. Peter, not just as the bishop of Rome.

2. The subject must be on a matter of faith and morals.

3. The teaching must be binding on all the faithful.

4. The pope must declare the teaching to be definitive.

Vatican I only met for a brief time before being interrupted by the outbreak of the Franco-Prussian War. French troops who were guarding Rome left to fight the Prussians, allowing Italian nationalists to seize the city in 1870. Pope Pius IX suspended the council indefinitely, and it was not officially closed until just before the opening of the Second Vatican Council.

7. *What was the Kulturkampf? Why was it instituted, and how was it defeated?*

Otto von Bismarck, president of Prussia and later chancellor of the Northern German Federation, wanted a strong, centralized German nation, and he saw the southern Catholic states, such as Bavaria and the Rhineland, as obstacles to his unification plan. He launched a propaganda war against the

Faith, putting Catholic schools under state supervision, expelling the Jesuits and other religious orders, and enforcing civil marriage over sacramental marriage. He also imitated previous rebellions against the Church by imprisoning bishops and priests, closing monasteries, and seizing Church lands.

In 1875, Pope Bl. Pius IX declared that German Catholics did not have to obey any anti-Catholic law. The laity held tightly to their faith, and Catholic representation in Parliament actually doubled. Eventually these laws were no longer enforced, and Pope Leo XIII was able to reach an agreement with Bismarck. The State retained control over public education and clerical appointments. The Church regained control of her seminaries and again enjoyed the freedom to publicly practice the Faith. A short while later, the Jesuits were allowed to return. Thus, in the end, the Church won the *Kulturkampf* through the perseverance of the Popes and the devoted obedience and dedication of the German laity.

D. Application

Discussion Leaders: If time permits, ask the group members to share their personal responses to the application question.

Despite the warnings of the Popes, Modernism is still with us today. In modern Western culture, science always trumps faith, miracles are considered myths, Scripture is treated as a fairy tale, atheism is considered intellectual, morality is completely relative, and religion must be separated from the State. Where do you encounter modernism in your own life? What can you do to fight this error?

Close with the prayer found in the Leader's Guide.

E. Wrap-up

1. *What is the color of this time period? How can you remember it?*

    Remember the Revolutions & Modernism time period by its color, gray: it symbolizes the intellectual confusion that gripped the Church and Western civilization as well as the clouds of industrialization.

2. *What is the main theme of this period?*

    The main theme of the Revolutions & Modernism period is how intellectual confusion brought Europe away from her Catholic roots.

3. *Write a one- or two-sentence summary of the Revolutions & Modernism period in order to recall the main events of Church history during this time.*

    Answers will vary but they should contain most of the main events listed on the *Epic* Church History Timeline chart.

A World at War

A JOURNEY THROUGH CHURCH HISTORY

A. Review the Context

Discussion Leaders: Make sure everyone has their *Epic* Church History Timeline chart to use when discussing questions about the time period. Briefly go over the other sections of the chart especially the Events & Influences section so that you can situate the story of the Church in the larger story of the world.

B. Learn the Story

Discussion Leaders: Unless there are comments or questions about Steve Weidenkopf's presentation, dive into answering the discussion questions in Section C.

C. Take a Deeper Look

1. *World War I was a barbaric conflict that originated almost by happenstance. Why did Europe tear itself apart in this bloody war?*

    Politically, the Great War began because the intricate and interwoven military alliances entered into by the major European states were triggered by the assassination of the crown prince of the Austro-Hungarian Empire. The nations of Europe had spent the last half of the 19th and early part of the twentieth century devoting large percentages of their gross domestic product to the military, Britain and Germany, in particular, raced each other in the building and outfitting of battleships and other naval vessels. Ultimately, though, there is no satisfying temporal reason for why the First World War happened or for why the war progressed as it did. The eminent military historian, John Keegan said, "The First World War is a mystery. Its origins are mysterious. So is its course." The war produced devastating consequences for Europe. Large numbers of her male youth were senselessly slaughtered and a deadly influenza pandemic reduced even more of the population. Spiritually, one can discern the hands of the Evil One in the carnage who desired to tear Europe away from the Church by hoping to breed an international sense of dread and despair in a benevolent God. The war and its devastation were also a direct consequence of industrialization, and the dehumanizing philosophy and worldview of the Enlightenment and modernism.

2. *What was the message delivered by the Blessed Virgin Mary at Fatima? What signs did God give to show that the apparitions of Fatima were both authentic and important?*

    The Virgin Mary told the three Portuguese children, Jacinta, Francisco, and Lucia, that God was greatly offended by the many sins of the world. She asked for the children and all Catholics to pray the Rosary daily, to make personal sacrifices for the conversion of sinners, and she asked for the consecration of Russia to her Immaculate Heart.

    Supernatural marks verify the authenticity of Fatima. Our Lady of Fatima not only predicted the ending of World War I, but she also predicted that World War II would begin during the reign of Pope Pius XI. The lives of the children after Fatima also lend evidence to the authenticity of the apparitions. Rather than attempt to become celebrities or make money from Fatima, the children went on to live simple, humble lives. After much suffering, Jacinta and Francisco both died at a very early age, as predicted by the Virgin Mary, and Lucia went on to become a Discalced Carmelite. Fifteen years after her death, the body of Jacinta was exhumed and was found to be completely incorrupt, like St. Bernadette and St. Catherine Labouré. The Church has beatified Francisco and Jacinta.

The greatest sign showing the divine approval of Fatima's message was the "miracle of the sun." The sun defied all known natural laws to "dance" in the sky before 70,000 eyewitnesses, some of whom were agnostic or atheist skeptics, and others who were as far as twenty-five miles away. It is the most widely witnessed miracle in all of history!

3. *What have you learned about the persecution of the Church in Mexico? Who was Blessed Miguel Pro?*

Tension had existed for some time between socialists and the Church in Mexico. In 1917, a socialist, anti-religious constitutional government was officially established. Starting in the 1920s, President Calles enacted harsh anti-Catholic policies that included the closing of 480 churches, schools, orphanages, and hospitals, the forfeiture of citizenship for Catholic bishops, and the arrest of clergy, as well as the public banishment of clerical clothing. Under the Calles regime, somewhere between 250,000 and 300,000 people were executed.

Bl. Miguel Pro was a Mexican priest martyred in 1927 by President Calles. Fr. Pro had gone into hiding, often wearing disguises to sneak around town and deliver the sacraments. A bomb was thrown at President Calles' car in November 1927. Fr. Pro's brother had once owned the car from which the bomb was thrown, so Fr. Pro and his brothers were arrested on trumped up charges of attempted assassination despite their airtight alibis. Once Calles learned that Fr. Pro was a Catholic priest, he ordered Pro's execution to be covered by journalists in order to use it later as propaganda aimed at demoralizing the population. Fr. Pro died forgiving his killers, his arms in the shape of the Cross, and Calles's plot backfired as the circulated pictures only inspired Mexican Catholics (they were later banned by the government). Pope John Paul II beatified Fr. Miguel Pro on September 25, 1988, and his feast day is November 23.

4. *During World War II, Hitler persecuted not only Jews but also millions of Catholics. What do you think motivated this persecution? Who were some of the Catholic martyrs of the Nazi prison camps?*

There are many reasons why Hitler persecuted Catholics in Germany as well as throughout the conquered territories of the Reich. The Church was a huge obstacle to Hitler's totalitarian grip on Germany. In exchange for recognition of the Church's rights throughout Germany (a promise Hitler soon reneged on), the Church agreed to disband the Catholic Center Party, National Socialism's most effective political opponent. Many Church leaders were outspoken in their defense of the Jews and other "undesirables" and provided a moral voice against the bigoted racial laws of Nazi Germany. Hitler desired the destruction of anyone or anything that stood in the way of his insane and demonic plans.

Thousands of German and Polish priests were sent to the concentration camps, especially Dachau, which was known as the "priest's camp." Some of the martyrs of the concentration camps have been beatified or canonized. Among them are Bl. Franz Jägerstätter, a layman who was beheaded for refusing to serve in the Wehrmacht, St. Teresa Benedicta of the Cross (Edith Stein), a famous author, Jewish convert, and Carmelite nun who died in the gas chamber at Auschwitz, and St. Maximilian Kolbe, founder of the Militia of the Immaculata, who offered his life in place of another prisoner at Auschwitz.

5. *Modern critics accuse the Catholic Church of cooperating with the Nazis and even condoning Nazi anti-Semitism. Pope Pius XII has been labeled as "Hitler's pope." How can you refute these absurd myths?*

Before other nations even paid attention to Nazi Germany, the Catholic Church was denouncing what she knew was a grave threat to the world. Pope Pius XI promulgated the anti-Nazi encyclical *Mit brennender Sorge* ("With Burning Anxiety") in 1937 where he condemned the policies of National Socialism, including its rabid anti-Semitism by bolding stating anti-Jewish bigotry is antithetical to the Christian Faith. He linked all Christians with the Jewish people by saying, "spiritually we are all Semites." Bishops and priests read the encyclical (which was later banned) from the pulpit of every Catholic Church in Germany.

Throughout the war, the Church aided the Allies (on the express orders of Pope Pius XII) by allowing Vatican diplomats to smuggle messages between Allied forces and Resistance fighters. Numerous "Righteous Gentiles" of the Church risked their lives to protect and rescue hundreds of thousands of Jews.

Eugenio Pacelli, the future Pius XII, was apostolic nuncio to Germany from 1917–1929. During his tenure he delivered forty-four public speeches containing attacks on National Socialism. As pope, he spoke out against Nazism and the killing of Jews and was even lauded by the *New York Times* in 1942 as a "lone voice crying out in the silence of a continent." He hid Jews in the Vatican, disguising many as Swiss guards and approved the issuance of fake sacramental records and hid 3,000 Jews in Castel Gandolfo, his summer residence. Many reputable historians estimate the number of Jewish lives saved as a direct result of Pius XII's and the Church's actions at around 860,000—about thirty percent of Jewish Holocaust survivors. Famous Jews such as Golda Meir and Albert Einstein heaped praise on Pius XII, and Israel Zolli, chief rabbi of Rome, converted to the Catholic Faith and took the baptismal name "Eugenio" to honor the Holy Father. The defamation of Pius XII's character was originated in the 1960s by a concerted Soviet propaganda campaign aimed at discrediting the papacy and reducing the influence of the Catholic Church. Numerous scholarly works have recently discredited the propaganda and provide a complete and documented picture of Pius' actions during the war.

6. *In many ways, the terrible wars of this time period are a direct result of the flourishing of modernism. What connections can you draw between the philosophy of modernism and the advent of the "modern war"?*

Modernism rejects the traditional worldview of Western civilization, denying the existence of the supernatural and lauding science as the only truth. The papacy's constant pleas for peace and moderation in warfare were ignored since modernism had divorced all religious ideas from political considerations. The Church ignored and the Faith belittled, the moral doctrines that guided warfare in the past were lost to the modern world. This abandonment of inalienable moral truths coincided with the rise of technologically-advanced weapons and the concept of total war. No historical precedent had been set for the use of the machine gun, mustard gas, aerial bombing or the specific targeting of major civilian population centers. Without the Church as a moral guide, these weapons were employed under a modernist mentality of "the ends justify the means." The culmination of this marriage of modernism and war can be seen in the bombing of entire cities in World War II, such as Dresden, Hiroshima, and Nagasaki. Civilian homes, schools, and even churches were destroyed in a clear violation of just war principles.

7. *History shows that invisible powers often hold great influence over human battles. Throughout this study, we have seen several examples of armies receiving divine aid at a critical moment: Constantine at the Milvian Bridge, the First Crusaders at Antioch and Jerusalem, St. Joan at Orléans, Don John at Lepanto, Sobieski at the Siege of Vienna. While this age was witness to the grace of God present in the millions of martyrs and saintly popes, there are hints of a dark power at play as well. What were some of the signs that suggest evil was aiding Lenin, Stalin, Hitler, and the other revolutionaries?*

The most obvious sign of diabolic influence is the brutal persecution of the Church present in every revolution throughout the twentieth century. The desecration of churches, execution of priests and religious, and criminalizing of the Faith often exceeded any possible rational justification and appear to be motivated in many cases by pure hatred. The rhetoric of the revolutionaries was often explicitly anti-Catholic, calling for the complete destruction or suppression of the Church and was based on an "Enlightened" and modernist philosophy of the rejection of the dignity of the human person and an embrace of the "culture of death." It is easy to see the presence of demonic influence in the degrading and dehumanizing political systems established in such places as Russia, Mexico, and Germany.

D. Application

Discussion Leaders: If time permits, ask the group members to share their personal responses to the application question.

The twentieth century was witness to the worst atrocities and bloodshed in human history, including the severe and constant persecution of the Church and her faithful. Not since the early days of the Church has she been called upon to offer such a witness. Although, for the most part, persecution through bloodshed has stopped, it can easily be re-started in a secular culture of death hostile to culture of life. Indeed, at the October 2007 beatification of 498 martyrs of the Spanish Civil War, Pope Benedict said, "the supreme witness of giving blood is not an exception reserved only to some individuals, but a realistic possibility for all Christian people." What are some things you can do to ensure you are ready in case you should face violent persecution in the future?

Close with the prayer found in the Leader's Guide.

E. Wrap-up

1. *What is the color of this time period? How can you remember it?*

   Remember the A World at War time period by its color, bright red: it symbolizes the rise of communism and fascism as well as the blood spilled during this new age of martyrs.

2. *What is the main theme of this period?*

   The main theme of the A World at War period is the widespread persecution of the Church and the subjection of the individual to the state by communist and fascist regimes.

3. *Write a one- or two-sentence summary of the A World at War period in order to recall the main events of Church history during this time.*

   Answers will vary but they should contain most of the main events listed on the *Epic* Church History Timeline chart.

The New Springtime

A. Review the Context

Discussion Leaders: Make sure everyone has their *Epic* Church History Timeline chart to use when discussing questions about the time period. Briefly go over the other sections of the chart especially the Events & Influences section so that you can situate the story of the Church in the larger story of the world.

B. Learn the Story

Discussion Leaders: Unless there are comments or questions about Steve Weidenkopf's presentation, dive into answering the discussion questions in Section C.

C. Take a Deeper Look

1. Why did Pope Bl. John XXIII call the Second Vatican Council? What was the council's main task?

Bl. John XXIII called the Second Vatican Council to develop ways to present the timeless teachings of the Faith anew to a skeptical modern world. Vatican II was to be a "New Pentecost." Filled with the Holy Spirit and renewed in grace, the Church would be prepared to take the Gospel message to a world in desperate need of God's love. The main task of the council was to demonstrate the validity of the teachings of the Church rather than condemn erroneous ones. Truly, the council was a unique and grace-filled event whose aim was to make the Gospel more accessible to a world racked by two costly and horrific world wars.

2. List the four major constitutions of the Second Vatican Council and provide the main points of each.

1. *Sacrosanctum Concilium* (Constitution on the Sacred Liturgy) – 1963

   - The reform and promotion of the liturgy

   - Emphasis on the importance of the Eucharist, proper liturgical worship, and the sacraments

   - Called for a renewal of the Roman Missal, with a greater acceptance of the use of the vernacular but the maintenance of Latin

2. *Lumen Gentium* (Dogmatic Constitution on the Church) – 1964

   - Discussion of the Church's inner nature & universal mission

   - The Church as a communion

   - Definition of the Church: "Christ, the one Mediator, established and continually sustains here on earth His holy Church, the community of faith, hope and charity, as an entity with visible delineation through which He communicates truth and grace to all."

   - Hierarchical structure of the Church

   - Charism of infallibility

- "Fullness of the means of salvation subsists within the Catholic Church; however, many elements of sanctification and of truth are found outside its visible confines."

- Universal call to holiness

- Last chapter devoted to Mary

3. *Dei Verbum* (Dogmatic Constitution on Divine Revelation) – 1965

    - Discusses what divine revelation is, how it is transmitted, how it is inspired and interpreted, and its role in the life of the Church.

    - Scripture is divinely inspired

    - "Scripture firmly, faithfully and without error teaches that truth that God, for the sake of our salvation, wished to see confided to the Sacred Scriptures."

    - "It is not from Sacred Scripture alone that the Church draws her certainty about everything which has been revealed."

    - Discussion of the role of the Magisterium

4. *Gaudium et Spes* (Pastoral Constitution on the Church in the Modern World) – 1965

    - An examination of the situation of modern man, the drama of life and the reality of the question: "Do you believe?"

    - Discusses the relationship between the Church and the world and the mission of the Church in the world

    - Focuses on "problems of special urgency" including marriage and the family, culture, economic and social life and peace

3. *It usually takes a generation for the decrees of a council to be implemented authentically. Is this statement true in reference to the Second Vatican Council?*

    As we have seen in prior time periods, the years after an ecumenical council are not always peaceful nor are the decrees of the council implemented properly or effectively. The same is true of the Second Vatican Council. Implementation was varied around the world. Some places, like Poland, were witness to an authentic implementation of the council documents and experienced an explosion in piety, devotion and a strengthened Church. Other areas, like Europe and the United States, experienced partially implementation at best and a "highjacking" of the council at worst. More than forty years after the close of the council, the Church in the Western world is beginning to see an emphasis on the authentic implementation of the council documents and a rejection of the "spirit of Vatican II" mentality. Pope John Paul II worked tirelessly to install a firm theological and philosophical foundation from which to understand the council and made its implementation one of the major goals of his pontificate. Benedict XVI has also focused on this crucial area; an area of much reflection and attention as Joseph Cardinal Ratzinger in his position as prefect of the Sacred Congregation for the Doctrine of the Faith.

4. *Two major social justice encyclicals were written during this time period, list them and provide the main points of each.*

    Pope Bl. John XXIII issued the encyclicals *Mater et Magistra* ("Mother and Teacher") and *Pacem in Terris* ("Peace on Earth") in 1961 and 1963, respectively. The main points of each are as follows:

    Mater et Magistra

- Written to commemorate the seventieth anniversary of Leo XIII's *Rerum Novarum*

- Discussion of the individual in relation to the state

    - State cannot abrogate rights of the individual

- Discussion of economics

    - Private ownership of goods and property good

- Economic and political rejection of communism (without mentioning it directly by name)

- Wealthy nations have obligation to help less developed nations

- Reaffirmation of objective morality

- Rejection of the "naked public square" worldview (i.e., enforcing the complete removal of God and religion from public life and discourse)

Pacem in Terris

- Peace is only achieved by following God's plan for human life, i.e. moral, virtuous living in imitation of Jesus Christ

- Discusses the proper relationships between individuals, humanity and the state, and among nations

- Every human being has the right to life and freedom

- The right to life is correlative with the right to defend life

- Condemns the "arms race" and encourages nations to settle disputes through negotiation

5. *Pope Paul VI promulgated* Humanae Vitae *in 1968. It is one of the most misunderstood and maligned papal writings in Church history. Why? What are its main points?*

Humanae Vitae was met with a wave of angry protests throughout Europe and the United States, perhaps the most famous protest occurred on the campus of Catholic University of America in Washington, D.C., led by professor Rev. Charles Curran (a priest of the Diocese of Rochester, NY). The encyclical was promulgated during the height of the cultural and sexual revolution of the 1960s, and its counter-cultural yet traditional teaching was not well received. Part of the reason for the poor reception can also be placed on the false expectation of a change in the teaching on contraception by many theologians and members of the clergy, who believed (because the "majority report" of the papal commission was leaked to the press) the pope would allow the use of the birth control pill. The backlash was unexpected and disturbing; so much so that Paul VI never wrote another encyclical (despite reigning for another ten years).

Although much criticism was levied against the document, it is a very beautiful teaching that explains the constant teaching of the Church on the subject of married love. Pope John Paul II would later provide a very compelling catechesis on *Humanae Vitae* as part of his larger catechetical work, popularly known as the "theology of the body."

Humanae Vitae encapsulates God's divine plan for marriage and human sexuality. Some of its main points are:

- Married couples are given a unique mission with God to bring new human life into the world

- Refutes the modern-day reasons for allowing the use of contraception

  - Over-population

  - Economic conditions

  - Role of woman in society

  - Sex does not have an inherent marital meaning

  - Man should use his knowledge to dominate and control nature

  - Contraception is not immoral if only used sparingly over the course of a marriage

- Marriage is a divine institution created by God for the good of the spouses and the procreation and education of children

- Married love mirrors God's love and is free, total, faithful, and fruitful

- Couples are called to exercise responsible parenthood, which, in part, means learning about the biological process of fertility, and making well-informed and generous decisions about their family size

- God has designed the woman's body with a cycle of fertility and with just and serious reasons, couples may make use of the infertile period to postpone pregnancy

- The marital act, by its nature has two inseparable elements: union and procreation

- Provides a list of immoral means of birth regulation

- Prophetically discusses the effects on human relations and society if contraception became widespread

- Ends with a series of pastoral directives aimed to call married couples to live this teaching; for clergy to preach it; for scientists and medical personnel to study and teach it.

6. *What are the "ecclesial movements"? List the names of a few of these groups. What is your impression of these groups?*

   Ecclesial movements are organizations within the Church, usually comprised of lay members (many also have priests and/or religious) that seek to live out the Second Vatican Council's "universal call to holiness." Many of these movements predate the council but grew in membership and acceptance after the council. Some of these movements include Opus Dei, the Legion of Christ, Focolare, Cursillo, and Neocatechumenal Way.

D. Application

Discussion Leaders: If time permits, ask the group members to share their personal responses to the application question.

The Second Vatican Council was a watershed moment in the lives of Catholics in the twentieth century. This gathering of bishops, led by the pope and guided by the Holy Spirit was filled with a sense of hope and renewal leading to the "New Springtime." In many places around the world the Council teachings were implemented successfully, in others (particularly Europe and the United States), a more difficult implementation resulted. What are your memories of the council? What has been your experience with its implementation? What can you do to aid the Church in successfully implementing the beautiful and inspired teachings of the Council?

Close with the prayer found in the Leader's Guide.

E. Wrap-up

1. *What is the color of this time period? How can you remember it?*

   Remember The New Springtime time period by its color, bright green: it symbolizes the springtime of renewal in the Church and the world fostered by the teachings of the Second Vatican Council.

2. *What is the main theme of this period?*

   The main theme of The New Springtime period is the calling of the Second Vatican Council and the desire to usher in a new era of reform and evangelization in the modern world.

3. *Write a one- or two-sentence summary of The New Springtime period in order to recall the main events of Church History during this time.*

   Answers will vary but they should contain most of the main events listed on the *Epic* Church History Timeline chart.

The Threshold of Hope & Conclusion

A. Review the Context

Discussion Leaders: Make sure everyone has their *Epic* Church History Timeline chart to use when discussing questions about the time period. Briefly go over the other sections of the chart especially the Events & Influences section so that you can situate the story of the Church in the larger story of the world.

B. Learn the Story

Discussion Leaders: Unless there are comments or questions about Steve Weidenkopf's presentation, dive into answering the discussion questions in Section C.

C. Take a Deeper Look

1. *What were the first public words uttered by John Paul II upon his election in 1978? Why do you think he choose those words?*

    Pope John Paul II greeted the faithful with the words, "Be not afraid," echoing the words uttered by angelic visitors in the Scriptures. The Holy Father wanted to reassure the faithful and the world that with Christ and in Christ, there is nothing to be afraid of, rather trusting in Him brings true joy, happiness and peace. These words found expression throughout John Paul II's pontificate. He embodied them by facing down the evil Soviet empire and traveling throughout the world spreading the Gospel. He invoked them when calling young people to be different and to choose the path least traveled in the modern world. He radiated the peace and security that comes from a deep relationship with Christ.

2. *List some of John Paul II's encyclicals. What are their topics? Which one is your favorite?*

    Pope John Paul II wrote fourteen encyclicals during his twenty-seven-year pontificate. They are listed below:

    1. ***Redemptor Hominis*, "The Redeemer of Man" – March 4, 1979**

        - Redemption and the human person

        - Dignity of the human person and human rights

    2. ***Dives in Misericordia*, "Rich in Mercy" – November 30, 1980**

        - The inexhaustible and indispensable mercy of God

    3. ***Laborem Exercens*, "On Human Work"– September 14, 1981**

        - The dignity and rights of those who work

        - Man is the proper subject of work

    4. ***Slavorum Apostoli*, "The Apostles of the Slavs" – June 2, 1985**

        - Honors Sts. Cyril and Methodius, who are the "connecting links or spiritual bridges between the Eastern and Western traditions, which both come together in the one great tradition of the universal church."

5. *Dominum et Vivificantem*, "On the Holy Spirit in the Life of the Church and the World" – **May 18, 1986**

   • The Holy Spirit – giver of Life

6. *Redemptoris Mater*, "The Mother of the Redeemer" – **March 25, 1987**

   • Importance and role of the Blessed Virgin Mary

   • Relationship between women and the Blessed Mother

7. *Sollicitudo Rei Socialis*, "The Social Concern of the Church" – **February 19, 1988**

   • Gap between the rich and poor

   • Reaffirms Church's social justice teaching

8. *Redemptoris Missio*, "The Mission of Christ the Redeemer" – **January 22, 1991**

   • Necessity of missionary evangelization and activity

9. *Centesimus Annus*, "On the Hundredth Anniversary of *Rerum Novarum*" – **May 1, 1991**

   • Discusses capitalism, the free market, unions and wages, unemployment, profit, atheism, class struggle, freedom, and private property

10. *Veritatis Splendor*, "The Splendor of Truth" – **August 6, 1993**

    • The foundations of moral theology

    • The bond between truth, freedom and the good

11. *Evangelium Vitae*, "The Gospel of Life" – **March 25, 1995**

    • Establishing the "culture of life"

    • Immorality of abortion and euthanasia and inability of states to legalize them

12. *Ut Unum Sint*, "On Commitment to Ecumenism" – **May 25, 1995**

    • The importance and role of ecumenism

13. *Fides et Ratio*, "Faith and Reason" – **September 14, 1998**

    • The relationship between faith and philosophy

    • Faith and reason are complimentary

14. *Ecclesia De Eucharistia*, "On the Eucharist in its Relationship to the Church" – **April 17, 2003**

    • The Eucharist and the life of the Church and the faithful

3. *What were the main themes of John Paul II's pontificate? Why did he choose those themes?*

Pope John Paul's main focus was the spreading of the Gospel so he constantly preached Christ and his salvific mission. Within that context, John Paul II's themes were the implementation of the Second Vatican Council, which he focused on through proper catechesis routed in the conciliar documents and through the promulgation of the *Catechism of the Catholic Church*. Another main theme was the proper relationship between man and woman and the love they share in marriage. This theme found expression in his Wednesday catecheses known as the "theology of the body." The modern world is in desperate need of the authentic teachings of the Church (and many elements within the Church were in need of correction hence the focus on the Council) as well as a proper understanding of marriage and sex.

4. *John Paul II greatly expanded the number of holy men and women honored by the Church as saints. Name some of these saints. Do you have a special devotion to one of these saints? If so, share the story of this saint and your devotion to him/her with the group.*

John Paul II canonized 482 men and women and beatified another 1,338. Answers will greatly vary on this question but here is a brief list of some of the saints and blesseds John Paul II gave the Church.

- St. Teresa Benedicta of the Cross (Edith Stein) – martyr
- St. Hedwig – Queen of Poland
- St. Jan Sarkander – martyr
- Holy Martyrs of Korea and Vietnam
- St. Padre Pio – mystic
- St. Faustina – Divine Mercy devotion
- Bl. Aloysius Stepinac – Croatian cardinal
- Bl. Damien de Veuster – missionary to lepers
- Bl. Elizabeth of the Trinity – mystic
- Bl. Marie Guyart – missionary to Quebec

5. *Some people have already begun to refer to Pope John Paul as "John Paul the Great." Who are the other "Great" popes in Church history? Should John Paul II be called "the Great"? Why or why not?*

There have been three pontiffs given the title "the great" by historians: Pope St. Leo I (440–461), St. Gregory I (590–604), and St. Nicholas I (858–867). There is no clear definition of what makes a pope "great," but the actions of the pontiff must be extraordinary not just in relation to the Church but to the world as well. All three of the "great" popes in Church history significantly contributed to the theology and practice of the Faith as well as provided temporal leadership in a time of grave crisis.

In this context, it is easy to place John Paul II in the company of the "greats." His theological contribution to the Faith is immense and will take years to fully unpack and develop. John Paul provided exceptional and heroic leadership during the course of his papacy especially in his role in bringing down the evil empire of communism.

There are those who will point to the perceived failings of John Paul II or his non-traditional expression of the papacy and some of those criticisms may be valid. As more years pass and more historians are able to take a critical review of the man and his papacy, a consensus will emerge and perhaps one day, future Catholics will refer to Karol Wojtyla as Pope John Paul the Great.

6. *What are some of the major issues facing the Church in the third millennium of the Faith?*

Answers can vary, but here are a few suggestions. The Church (and the world) is faced with the rise of militant Islam, a phenomenon that is understood and not surprising once one studies the history of the

Church and Western civilization. The Church faces significant demographic changes to the world as she progresses through the twenty-first century. The Western world as a whole is experiencing profound population loss. Most Western nations have a declining birth rate and will be unable to support their aging population in the foreseeable future. As an example, by 2050, sixty percent of Italians will not have a brother, sister, cousin, aunt, or uncle. As a result of the Enlightenment and two vicious world wars, Europe has moved away from her historic roots and left the Faith. Although there are signs of hope, the continent as a whole is deeply secular. In 2004, only eight percent of French citizens attend Mass regularly and nearly one-third profess no religion at all.

The Church is also faced with a catechetical crisis throughout the western world. Many do not know the Faith (because it has not been handed on to them) or know the Faith incompletely. Vocations to the priesthood and religious life have also declined and are even non-existent in many areas. There are signs of resurgence in some areas and that produces a sense of hope but the Church needs more men and women to answer that unique call. Lastly, the western world is in the midst of a cultural and historical amnesia. In some regards the term "Western civilization" barely resonates with modern man. Western culture embraces the "naked public square" where God is not permitted nor discussion of Faith is allowed.

Although there are many problems afflicting the western world, the non-western world, in terms of the Faith, is prospering and may one day provide the missionaries needed to restore Europe to her Christian roots.

7. *You are now at the conclusion of this study; answer the following questions about your twenty-week* Epic *journey:*

> *a. What time period(s) most interested you? Why?*
>
> *b. What is the most important thing you have learned studying Church history?*
>
> *c. What time period(s) would you like to delve deeper?*
>
> *d. Using your Epic chart, trace the twenty-one ecumenical councils, what can they tell you about the   story of the Church?*
>
> *e. What role can you play in the continuing story of the Church?*

Answers to these questions are highly individualistic but here are some thoughts on a few of them.

The one thing that is easily discernible from a study of Church history is the existence and actions of the Holy Spirit. If only a human institution, the Church would not be in existence today. Truly, the Holy Spirit has animated and guided the Church throughout her long history, preserving her from error and protecting her from evil.

A study of the ecumenical councils provides a microcosm of the history of the Church. Each council is situated in a unique historical context, which when understood, sheds light on the larger history of the Church and the world. The councils are dramatic events that shaped the Church and Western civilization. A study of them produces not only a firm understanding of the doctrines of the Church but also knowledge of her Popes and her epic story.

Each person has a unique role to play in the story of the Church. God has called each of us by name and given us individual gifts and talents to use for His greater glory. A fixture of our prayer life should focus on what His Will is for us and how best we can serve Him. Whatever our role, each of us has a responsibility to know our Faith, including the dramatic story of the Church. We need to know this story so we can more easily identify with the Church and be able to hand on her story to our family and friends.

D. Application

Discussion Leaders: If time permits, ask the group members to share their personal responses to the application question.

Pope John Paul II shaped the lives of many Catholics. Many young priests or those currently studying for the priesthood trace the origin of their vocation to John Paul II's witness and outreach to youth. Numerous families have chosen to name their sons John Paul in honor of the late Holy Father. His long reign and charismatic personality are some of the reasons for the tremendous devotion and love for the Polish Pope. What are your memories of Pope John Paul II? What actions or writings influenced your life the most? How has John Paul II's pontificate enriched your live as a Catholic?

Close with the prayer found in the Leader's Guide.

E. Wrap-up

1. *What is the color of this time period? How can you remember it?*

    Remember The Threshold of Hope time period by its color, Marian blue: this color is associated with the pontificate of Pope John Paul II who had a significant devotion to Our Lady and is also a color associated with the Blessed Mother; especially as Our Lady of Hope.

2. *What is the main theme of this period?*

    The main theme of The Threshold of Hope period is the pontificate of Pope John Paul II and the Church's advance into the Third Millennium.

3. *Write a one or two sentence summary of The Threshold of Hope period in order to recall the main events of Church History during this time.*

    Answers will vary but they should contain most of the main events listed on the *Epic Church History Timeline* chart.

APPENDIX

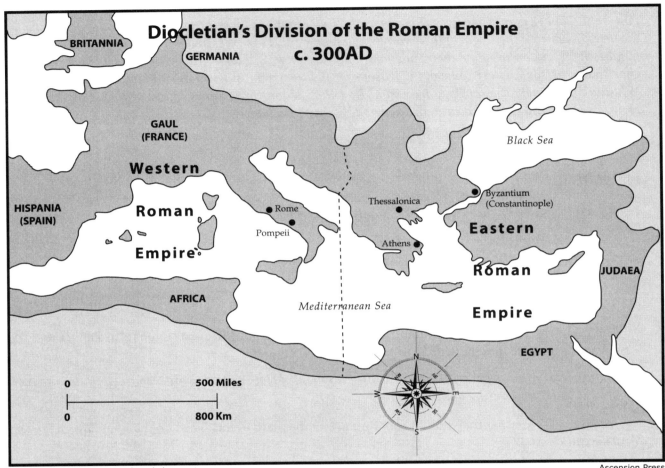

CHRISTIAN PERSECUTIONS IN THE ROMAN EMPIRE

Emperor	Dates	Persecution	Martyrs*
Nero	64 – 67	Rome destroyed by fire. A persistent rumor indicated Nero started the fire. In order to shift blame, he accused the Christians who were put to death in large numbers.	Sts. Peter & Paul
Domitian	95	Persecuted Christians throughout Empire, even members of the imperial family.	
Trajan	98 – 117	Christians were not to be sought out; however, those who were accused but offered sacrifice to pagan gods were spared. Those who refused to worship false gods and manifested their Christian faith were to be executed.	St. Ignatius of Antioch
Hadrian	117 – 138	Similar policy to Trajan	St. Telesphorus
Antonius Pius	138 – 161	Local persecutions	St. Polycarp
Marcus Aurelius	161 – 180	Local persecutions	St. Justin Martyr, Martyrs of Lyons
Septimus Severus	193 – 211	Forbade new converts to the Faith	St. Felicity & St. Perpetua
Alexander Severus	222 – 235	Local persecutions	St. Cecilia
Maximinus Thrax	235 – 238	Ordered Church leaders to be put to death	Sts. Pontian & Hippolytus
Decius	249 – 251	All inhabitants of Empire were required to perform an act of worship to pagan gods. Those who refused were executed.	St. Fabian, St. Agatha, St. Denis & companions
Gallus	251 – 253	Continued Decius' persecution	St. Cornelius
Valerian	257 – 259	Issued edict in 257 ordering all bishops, priests and deacons to sacrifice to pagan gods. Forbade visits to cemeteries and Christian assemblies.	St. Cyprian, St. Lawrence, St. Sixtus II, St. Tarsicius
Diocletian	303 – 305	Arrested and executed Christians who refused to worship pagan gods. Destroyed churches, burned sacred books, and forbade Christian assemblies.	St. Sebastian, Sts. Marcellinus & Peter, St. Lucy, Sts. Cosmas & Damien
Galerius	305 – 311	Continued Diocletian persecutions	St. Agnes, St. Catherine of Alexandria

* Selected martyrs
Bolded Emperors = Major Persecutions

MAJOR HERESIES & SCHISMS BY TIME PERIOD

Time Period	Date(s)	Heretic/ Heresy/ Schism	Teachings	Church's Response
Persecution	144	Marcion	Denied human nature of Christ; Developed dichotomy between the Old and New Testaments	Writings of St. Justin Martyr, St. Irenaeus, Tertullian, St. Hippolytus
Persecution	Ancient World – Present	Gnosticism	Dualist. Matter = bad; Spirit = good. Denied/Rejected Incarnation, Eucharist, Marriage	Writings of St. Justin Martyr, St. Irenaeus, Tertullian, St. Hippolytus
Persecution	2nd & 3rd Centuries	Modalism	Denied Separate Persons of the Trinity; God appears in *mode* of Father, Son & Holy Spirit	Writings of Tertullian, St. Hippolytus
Persecution	251	Novatian	Disagreed with papal policy of clemency toward those who lapsed during persecution. Followers elected him anti-pope	Novatian and followers excommunicated by Pope Cornelius
Persecution	260	Paul of Samosata	God is One Person not Three. Christ not real but *adopted* Son of God	Local Synods condemn teachings; driven from See of Antioch by civil power
Persecution	2nd & 3rd Centuries	Montanus	Sins after baptism not forgiven. Personal revelation equal in authority to Scripture and Tradition.	Writings of St. Hippolytus, St. Epiphanius & St. Irenaeus
Conversion & Councils	311 – 411	Donatism	Validity of sacrament depends on worthiness of minister; no clemency for those who lapsed	Condemned by Pope Miltiades; local Council of Arles (314); St. Augustine
Conversion & Councils	320 – 600	Arianism	Denied divinity of Christ; Jesus is created not eternal	Council of Nicaea; St. Athanasius

Conversion & Councils	5th Century	Pelagianism	Denied necessity of Grace; Denied Original Sin	St. Augustine; local Council of Carthage (418)
Conversion & Councils	431	Nestorius	Christ is 2 persons; Mary is not the Mother of God	St. Cyril of Alexandria; Pope Celestine I; Council of Ephesus
Conversion & Councils	451	Eutyches	Monophysitism – Christ has only one nature	St. Flavin; Pope St. Leo the Great; Council of Chalcedon
Missionaries & the Emperor	553	Three Chapters	Writings of three theologians could be construed as Nestorian; Question over who decides orthodoxy; Pope or Emperor	2nd Council of Constantinople
Missionaries & the Emperor	7th Century	Monothelitism	Christ has only one Will.	3rd Council of Constantinople
Missionaries & the Emperor	8th & 9th Centuries	Iconoclasm	Destruction of sacred images	Pope Gregory II; Pope Gregory III; St. John Damascene; Empress Irene; 2nd Council of Nicaea (787)
Missionaries & the Emperor	Mid-9th Century	Photius	Photius, Patriarch of Constantinople, excommunicates Pope Nicholas and enters into schism	4th Council of Constantinople (869)
Crusaders & Scholars	1054	Byzantines The Great Schism	Michael Cerularius, Patriarch of Constantinople, enacts anti-Latin measures. Papal legates excommunicate Cerularius who then excommunicates Pope	Paul VI and Patriarch Athenagoras annulled the excommunications in 1965; Efforts of Pope John Paul II; schism unhealed

Crusaders & Scholars	11th – 13th Centuries	Albigensianism (aka Catharism)	Dualist. Matter = bad; Spirit = good. Denied/Rejected Incarnation, Eucharist, Marriage; established counter-church	Dominicans & the Inquisition; Albigensian Crusade
Weak Leaders & Schism	1324 – 1384	John Wyclif	Denied Transubstantiation; attacked papal authority; Church cannot own property; *sola scriptura*	Condemned by Pope Gregory XI; London Synod (1377)
Weak Leaders & Schism	1378 – 1417	The Great Western Schism	Multiple papal claimants causes disunity and confusion in Christendom	Council of Constance; Pope Martin V
Weak Leaders & Schism	14th – 15th Centuries	Conciliarism	Council superior in authority than the Pope	5th Lateran Council (1512 – 1517)
Weak Leaders & Schism	1369 – 1415	Jan Hus	Denied Papal jurisdiction over the universal Church; Denied Sacred Tradition as element of the Deposit of Faith; Church had no authority to restrict Communion under one species to laity	Council of Constance (1414 – 1418)
Protestors & Defenders & The Catholic Reformation	1517 – present	Protestantism	*Sola Scriptura*, justification by faith alone; Denied papal authority, free will, sacrificial nature of priesthood, sacraments, etc.	Council of Trent; Jesuits; Saints
Revolutions & Modernism	18th Century – present	Modernism	Embraces every heresy; anti-Catholic world view	*Syllabus of Errors*; 1st Vatican Council (1869 – 1870); *Pascendi Dominici Gregis*
The Threshold of Hope	1988	Marcel Lefebvre	Rejection of *Novus Ordo*; 2nd Vatican Council	Excommunication; *Eccelsia Dei*; Indult Mass

THE 21 ECUMENICAL COUNCILS OF THE CHURCH

#	Council	Date(s)	Heresy/Issues	Teaching of Church
1	Nicaea	325	*Arianism* • Denial of divinity of Christ • *Homoiousios* = of **like** substance	Jesus Christ is true God and true man. "One in being (consubstantial; *homoousios* = of **same** substance) with the Father."
2	Constantinople	381	*Pneumatomachi (Macedonianism)* • Denial of divinity of the Holy Spirit (He is creation of the Son)	Reaffirmed teachings of Nicea. Holy Spirit is a divine person.
3	Ephesus	431	*Nestorianism* • Christ is two persons • Mary is not Mother of God	Christ is one divine person Mary is therefore the Mother of God.
4	Chalcedon	451	*Monophysitism* • Christ has one nature • Human nature absorbed by divine nature	Christ has two natures, human and divine, "not to be confused, changed, separated or divided." "Hypostatic union" = Christ is one person (*hypostasis*); human and divine nature united
5	Contantinople II	553	Three Chapters Theological writings tainted by Nestorianism	Reaffirmed teachings of Ephesus & Chalcedon
6	Constantinople III	680	*Monothelitism* • Christ has one will • Human will absorbed by divine will	Christ has two wills: human & divine
7	Nicaea II	787	*Iconoclasm & Adoptionism* • Use of images in sacred art = idolatry • Christ not Son of God by nature – only thru adoption	Use of images in sacred art not idolatry. Images are used to help us contemplate divine mystery. Reaffirmed "hypostatic union"
8	Constantinople IV	869	*Photian Schism*	Deposed Photian – ended schism between East & West

9	**Lateran I**	1123	*Investiture Controversy*	Confirmed Concordat of Worms (1122)
10	**Lateran II**	1139	Various theological heresies	Reaffirmed baptism of infants; sacraments of Holy Orders, Marriage, Eucharist
11	**Lateran III**	1179	*Albigensianism*	Condemned Albigensianism – matter is good; Papal elections require 2/3 vote of cardinals
12	**Lateran IV**	1215	Various heresies about the Eucharist	Instituted "Easter Duty" – annual reception of Eucharist; confession Used term "transubstantiation"
13	**Lyons I**	1245	*Frederick II – HRE*	Excommunicated & deposed Frederick II
14	**Lyons II**	1274	*East – West Schism*	Temporary union of East & West; Regulations for papal conclaves
15	**Vienne**	1311 – 1312	*Knights Templar*	Suppressed Knights
16	**Constance**	1414 – 1418	*Great Western Schism Jan Hus*	Ended Schism – elected Pope Martin V *Hus Condemned*
17	**Florence**	1431 – 1445	*Conciliarism*	Reaffirmed papal primacy; Temporary union of East & West
18	**Lateran V**	1512 – 1517	*Ecclesiastical Abuses*	Prohibited Absenteeism; Pluralism; Simony; Clericalism
19	**Trent**	1545– 1549; 1551– 1552; 1562– 1563	*Protestantism*	Reaffirmed Catholic doctrine on Scripture & Tradition, grace, sin, justification, Mass as a sacrifice, purgatory, indulgences. Initiated Catholic reformation; reformed clergy, instituted seminary structure; reform of liturgy; Called for universal catechism

| 20 | Vatican I | 1869 – 1870 | *"Enlightenment" Faith & Reason* | Condemned notions that faith & reason are opposed. Defined nature & jurisdiction of papal infallibility & primacy |
| 21 | Vatican II | 1962 – 1965 | *The Modern World* | Reaffirmed Church teaching on divine revelation; mystery of the Church. Called for reform of liturgy, application of Christian revelation/mysteries to modern, unbelieving world |

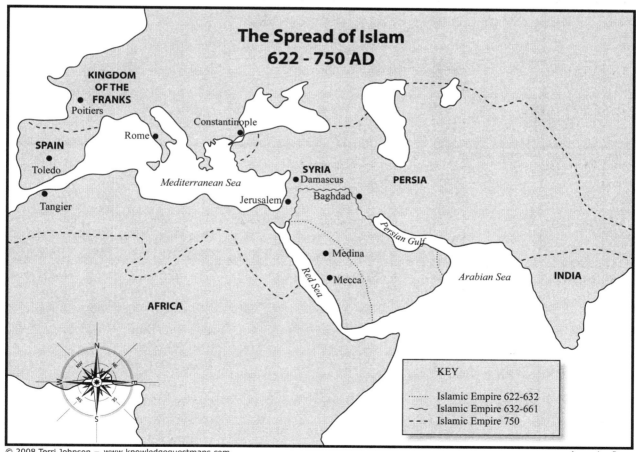

© 2008 Terri Johnson – www.knowledgequestmaps.com

Ascension Press

Ascension Press

A CHRONOLOGY OF THE CRUSADES

Background to the Crusades: The Rise of Militant Islam

Dates	Event
610 – 632	Muhammad receives "revelations" from archangel Gabriel
622	Hejira (flight) of Muhammad from Mecca to Medina
627	Mecca conquered by force
630 – 632	Arabian Peninsula conquered
632	Death of Muhammad
634 – 638	Conquest of Syria & Palestine; Jerusalem taken
641	Egypt conquered
c. 652	Muslims raiding coastal towns in Italy
700	North Africa conquered
710 – 720	March through Spain
732	Battle of Poitiers – Charles Martel ("The Hammer") defeats Muslim army and halts advance through France
827	Muslims begin conquest of Sicily (retaken in 1091)
846	Muslims raid Rome
867 – 1025	Byzantine Empire reclaims Syria, Palestine and Jerusalem
1009	Destruction of the Church of the Holy Sepulchure
1071	Muslims (Seljuks) defeat Byzantine army at Manzikert – Emperor Romanus Diogenes taken prisoner
1085	Toledo is retaken by Alfonzo VI of Castile

The Era of the Crusades

Dates	Events
1095	Pope Urban II preaches First Crusade at Council of Clermont (27 November)
1096 – 1102	**The First Crusade**
1099	Jerusalem reclaimed by Christian army (15 July)
1120	Knights Templar founded
1126	Knights of St. John (Hospitallers) militarized
1146 – 1147	St. Bernard preaches the crusade
1147 – 1149	**The Second Crusade**
1187	Battle of Hattin – Saladin defeats Christian army (4 July)
1187	Jerusalem falls to Saladin (2 October)
1189 - 1192	**The Third Crusade**
1198	Teutonic Order founded
1201 – 1205	**The Fourth Crusade**
1204	Crusader sack of Constantinople (12 – 15 April)

1209 – 1229	The Albigensian Crusade
1212	The Children's Crusade
1218 – 1221	**The Fifth Crusade**
1228 – 1229	**The Sixth Crusade - Frederick II**
1229	Jerusalem restored to Christians via a treaty
1244	Jerusalem lost to Muslims
1248 – 1254	**The First Crusade of King St. Louis IX**
1269 – 1272	**The Second Crusade of King St. Louis IX**
1291	City of Acre (last Christian stronghold) falls to the Muslims

Aftermath of the Crusader Era

Dates	Events
1453	Constantinople falls to the Turks
1492	Granada falls to crusaders – reconquest of Spain accomplished
1522	Hospitallers surrender Rhodes
1529	Muslims besiege Vienna
1565	Siege of Malta – Hospitallers hold out against large Muslim force
1571	Battle of Lepanto – Holy League fleet under Don Juan of Austria defeats superior Muslim fleet (7 October)
1588	Crusade against England – the Spanish armada
1683	Muslim siege of Vienna broken by Polish king Jan Sobieski (11 September)

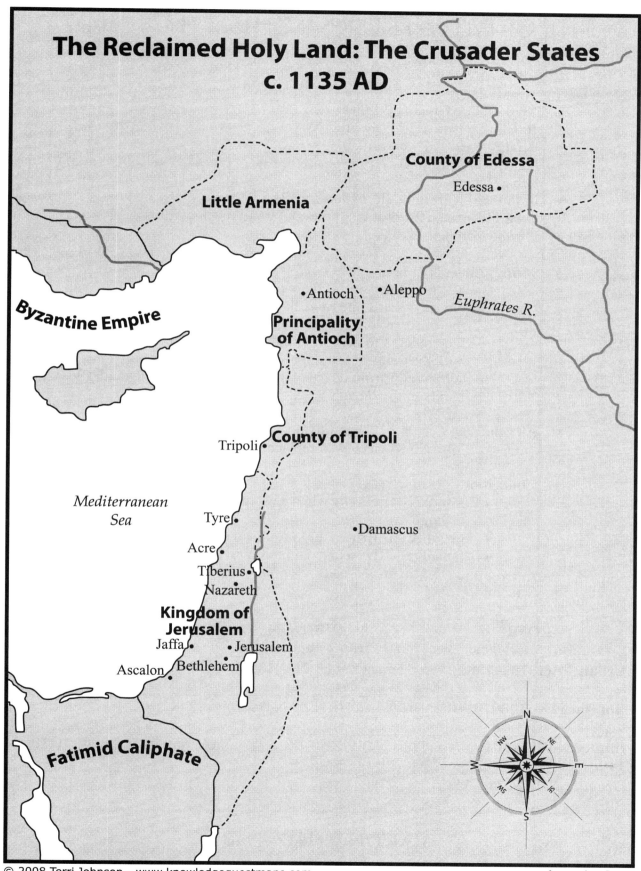

The Reclaimed Holy Land: The Crusader States
c. 1135 AD

Ascension Press

THE GREAT WESTERN SCHISM (1378 – 1417)

Background:
- 1378 – Pope Gregory XI dies
- 16 Cardinals meet (11 are French)
- Urban VI elected – an Italian
- French cardinals leave Rome – say they were forced by a Roman mob to elect Urban VI.
- In France – cardinals elect Clement VII
- Urban VI excommunicates "anti-pope" and French cardinals
- Europe is in Schism

- 1406 - University of Paris faculty calls for end of schism
- 1409 – Pisa – the French and Italian cardinals meet
  - o Gregory XII (Pope) and Benedict XIII (anti-pope) appear before the convocation
  - o they refused to accept authority of gathering
  - o both excommunicated by Cardinals
  - o combined cardinals elect another anti-pope – Alexander V
- Three Claimants to the Papacy!

- Alexander V dies after 11 months
  - o John XXIII elected to replace him – lives in Pisa

- Council of Constance (1414)
  - o John XXIII flees city when it was apparent he would not be confirmed as Pope
  - o Gregory XII (true pope) promised to abdicate and did
  - o Benedict XIII – refused to step down – council deposed him
  - o 1417 Martin V – elected Pope
- Schism over

ROME *(the true Popes)*	AVIGNON *(anti-popes)*	PISA *(anti-popes)*
Urban VI (1378 – 1389)	Clement VII (1378 – 1393)	
Boniface IX (1389 – 1404)	Benedict XIII (1393 – 1415)	
Innocent VII (1404 – 1406)		Alexander V (1409 – 1410)
Gregory XII (1406 – 1415)		John XXIII (1410 – 1415)

MARTIN V (1417 – 1431)

THE COUNCIL OF TRENT (1545 – 1563)

Sessions	Dates	Pope	Teachings
1 – 10	1545 – 1547	Paul III	† Endorsed Nicene Creed † Vulgate † Defined Nature of Original Sin & Justification † Began doctrinal review of sacraments o Defined Baptism & Confirmation
11 – 16	1551 – 1552	Julius III	† Definition of Eucharist (doctrine of Real Presence), Penance, Extreme Unction
17 – 25	1562 – 1563	Pius IV (St. Charles Borromeo)	† Additional teachings on the Eucharist (Communion under both species and Communion of little children) † Definition of Holy Orders, Matrimony † Defined Purgatory, veneration of saints, relics, sacred art, indulgences † Called for revision & publication of Roman Missal, Divine Office † Authorized formation of a universal Catechism † Required bishops to reside at least nine months of the year in diocese – if absent for more than six months = deposed. † Called for creation of seminaries † Priests to reside in parish & wear clerical garb

THE BREAKING OF CHRISTENDOM:
A CHRONOLOGY OF MAJOR PROTESTANT GROUPS

Group	Date Founded	Founder(s)
Lutheran	1517	Martin Luther
Anabaptists	1521	Nicholas Storch, Thomas Münzer, John Denk, Balthasar Hubmaier, Felix Mänz, Conrad Grebel
Anglican	1534	Henry VIII
Calvinist	1536	John Calvin
Mennonites	1536	Menno Simons
Presbyterian	1560	John Knox
Congregationalist	1582	Robert Brown
Baptist	1605	John Smyth
Dutch Reformed	1628	Michaelis Jones
Methodist	1744	John & Charles Wesley
Unitarian	1774	Theophilus Lindley
Mormon*	1829	Joseph Smith
Seventh-day Adventism	1860	William Miller, Hiram Edson, Joseph Bates, Ellen Gould White
Salvation Army	1865	William Booth
Jehovah's Witnesses*	1879	Charles Taze Russell
Christian Scientist	1879	Mary Baker Eddy
Pentecostal	1900	Charles Parham, William Seymour
Fundamentalism	1909	Various

* Theologically, the Church of Jesus Christ of Latter-day Saints (the Mormons) and the Jehovah's Witnesses are not Christian and therefore not truly Protestant Groups.

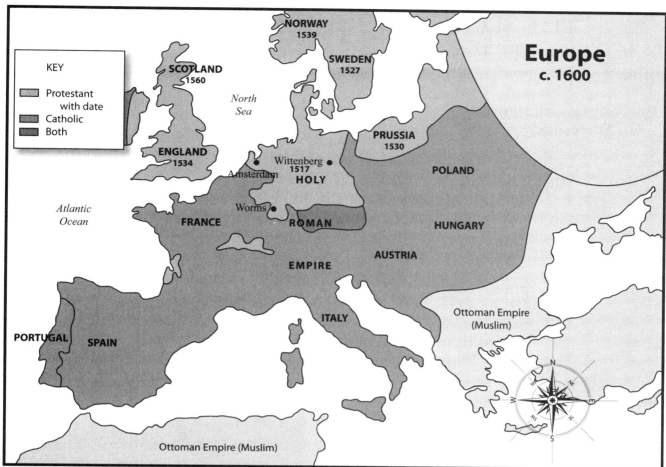

Ascension Press

THE SIXTEEN DOCUMENTS OF THE SECOND VATICAN COUNCIL

The Four Constitutions:

1. Sacrosanctum Concilium – December 4, 1963

> English title = The Constitution on the Sacred Liturgy
>
> Summary: The reform and promotion of the liturgy of the Church, which is the "summit toward which the activity of the Church is directed... the fount from which all her power flows" (SC, 10). Also discussed the proper manner in which we, the faithful, come to the liturgy to celebrate: "before men can come to the liturgy they must be called to faith and to conversion" (SC, 9). First document of the Council.

2. Lumen Gentium – November 21, 1964

> English title = The Dogmatic Constitution on the Church
>
> Summary: An answer to the world to the question "who does the Church say she is?" Document intends to show the Church in her nature, as "mystery." A statement of the awareness and reality of the Church's mission on carrying out the Salvific mission of Christ and His mandate to make disciples of all peoples.

3. Dei Verbum – November 18, 1965

> English title = The Dogmatic Constitution on Divine Revelation
>
> Summary: The assessment of the Church's role in fulfilling the words of St. John: "What we have seen and heard we proclaim in turn to you so that you may share the life with us." (1 John 1:3). Discusses what divine revelation is, how it is transmitted, how it is inspired and interpreted, and its role in the life of the Church.

4. Gaudium et Spes – December 7, 1965

> English title = The Pastoral Constitution on the Church in the Modern World
>
> Summary: An examination of the situation of modern man, the drama of life and the reality of the question: "do you believe?" Discusses the relationship between the Church and the world and the mission of the Church in the world.

The Decrees:

5. Inter Mirifica – December 4, 1963

> English title = Decree on the Instruments of Social Communication
>
> Summary: Discusses Church's obligation to employ the means of social communication to announce the Gospel and to teach men how to use them properly.

6. Unitatis Redintegratio – November 21, 1964

> English title = Decree on Ecumenism
>
> Summary: Urgently calls for the restoration of Christian unity throughout the world and sets forth Catholic principles on ecumenism.

7. *Orientalium Ecclesiarum* – November 21, 1964
   English title = Decree on the Eastern Catholic Churches
   Summary: Presents the dignity and distinctiveness of the Eastern rites of the Catholic Church, which are a bridge to those Eastern Christian Churches not in full communion with the Catholic Church.

8. *Christus Dominus* – October 28, 1965
   English title = Decree on the Pastoral Office of Bishops in the Church
   Summary: Reflects on the comment of Pope Paul VI that a bishop must be the "image of the Father and the image of Christ." Emphasizes the prophetic and pastoral dimensions of the office of bishop.

9. *Optatum Totius* – October 28, 1965
   English title = Decree on the Training of Priests
   Summary: Reaffirms traditional means of priestly training and formation and calls for new regulations in harmony with council documents and the changed conditions of our times.

10. *Perfectae Caritatis* – October 28, 1965
    English title = Decree on the Appropriate Renewal of the Religious Life
    Summary: Discusses the consecrated life as "distinctly characterized by the profession of vows," and as a "perfect life according to the teaching and example of Jesus Christ." This decree is intended to make provisions for the needs of those who accept the life and discipline of chastity, poverty, and obedience. Religious life is ordered, before all else, to the following of Christ.

11. *Apostolicam Actuositatem* – November 18, 1965
    English title = Decree on the Apostolate of the Laity
    Summary: Realizing the Holy Spirit is moving the laity to a deeper awareness of their responsibilities in the service of Christ and His Church, the Council explains the nature of the lay apostolate, its character and variety of its forms. It states the principles and gives pastoral directives for the more effective exercise of the lay apostolate.

12. *Presbyterorum Ordinis* – December 7, 1965
    English title = Decree on the Ministry and Life of Priests
    Summary: Council wished to give more effective support to the ministry of priests. This decree is intended to make better provisions for the life of priests in these rapidly changing times.

13. *Ad Gentes Divinitus* – December 7, 1965
    English title = Decree on the Church's Missionary Activity
    Summary: Outlines the principles of missionary activity. Discusses missionary nature of the Church. The Church desires to make herself fully present to all men and people in order to lead them to faith, freedom and the peace of Christ by the example of her life and teaching and by the sacraments.

The Declarations:

14. *Gravissimum Educationis* – October 28, 1965

 English title = Declaration on Christian Education

 Summary: Sets forth fundamental principles concerning Christian education, especially in regards to schools.

15. *Nostra Aetate* – October 28, 1965

 English title = Declaration on the Relationship of the Church to Non-Christian Religions

 Summary: The Church has a duty to foster unity and charity among all peoples. The Church states she "rejects nothing of what is true and holy in these [non-Christian] religions... Yet she proclaims and is in duty bound to proclaim without fail, Christ, who is the Way, the Truth, and the Life."

16. *Dignitatis Humanae* – December 7, 1965

 English title = Declaration on Religious Liberty

 Summary: A landmark document declaring that all people should be free to seek out God and to worship Him, both individually and corporately, without restriction or coercion while respecting the "just requirements of the public order." "...it leaves intact the traditional Catholic teaching on the moral duty of individuals and societies towards the true religion and the one Church of Christ" (DH, 1).

A KEY TO THE PERIOD COLORS

1. Mustard Seed — Mustard Yellow — parable of the Kingdom of God

2. Persecution — Dark Red — blood of the martyrs

3. Conversion & Councils — White — Empire clothed white in Christ

4. Missionaries & the Emperor — Purple — Royalty of the Holy Roman Emperor

5. Crusaders & Scholars — Navy Blue — Color of France – land of crusaders

6. Weak Leaders & Schism — Black — dark time in the Church

7. Protestors & Defenders — Orange — William of Orange *(traditional Protestant color)*

8. The Catholic Reformation — Gold — holy saints reform the Church

9. Revolutions & Modernism — Gray — clouds of industrialization & intellectual confusion

10. A World at War — Bright Red — Color of Fascism and Communism

11. The New Springtime — Bright Green — springtime of renewal in the Church

12. The Threshold of Hope — Marian blue — Pope John Paul II and Mary – Our Lady of Hope

MARCHING FORWARD ON YOUR EPIC JOURNEY

Congratulations! You have successfully journeyed through your twenty-week study of Church history. Hopefully, this study has provided an excellent foundation for your furthered exploration of the rich and vast history of the Church.

We urge you to continue your study of Church history by picking up some of the selections of the recommended readings. Keep your *Epic* chart and bookmark close by as you read through these works. Remember that the key to understanding history is to view it through the lens of the divine drama that it is. Try to see God working through the lives of the characters in the epic story of the Church. Place yourself in the time period and contemplate how you would handle certain situations.

Church history is not just the recitation of popes, people, places, and events; it is a story (His-story) of adventure, intrigue, rebellion, reform, and devotion. The study of Church history is crucial to our lives as Catholics. The story of our Church should resonate with our identity as Catholics. It is our family history. In order to shape the future of our world and our Church, we must know our past. Keep checking the *Epic* website (www.CatholicTimeline.com) for information on future products, including in-depth period studies that will help guide you along the epic journey of Church history.

Learn the story of the Church and re-tell it to your family and friends!

May the Lord and Our Lady bless and intercede for you and your family.

ACKNOWLEDGMENTS

I offer my sincerest thanks and love to my wonderful wife, Kasey and my beautiful children, Madison, Maximilian, Thérèse, Luke, and Jeb. Your support and love brought this project to completion. I heartily thank Vince Cornell for his assistance in writing a good portion of this study guide. Elizabeth Doerr Gorney's work, support, and professionalism were instrumental. Thanks are also due to the many friends and students whose prayers sustained me through the many hours of writing: special thanks are due to my brothers in Christ, Sean Dalton, Joe Burns, and Greg Erkens. I also greatly appreciate the efforts of Carol Hertz. I am saddened that my grandfather, Burt Weidenkopf passed away during the production of the manuscript. His love and support throughout my life helped to prepare me to complete this work. His life was an epic adventure and he is truly missed. Finally, I give thanks to the Blessed Virgin Mary whose maternal love and intercession guided me in this journey.